COMPLETE COORDINATED SCIENCE

Biology

Stan Cooper   Will Deloughry
Mike Hiscock   Philip Naylor

HEINEMANN

Contents

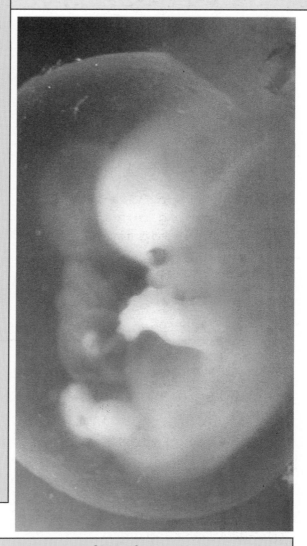

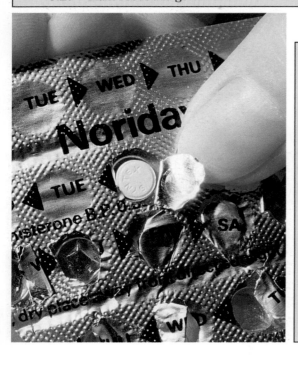

Life and life processes

What's this book about?

This book explains and investigates the activities which are carried out by living organisms, how these activities are controlled and how organisms affect each other and their environment. It is a study of *life and life processes*.

In this study four central questions are explored. These are:

What processes are essential for life?

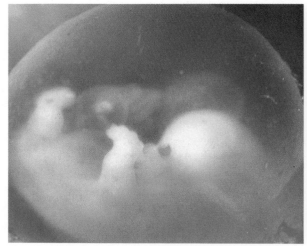

It is amazing to think that you started life from a single cell smaller than the size of a pin head. Yet this minute cell developed into you – a very complex and highly organised organism. Like other animals and plants you can obtain and use energy, remove waste materials, grow and reproduce, and respond to changes taking place around and inside you. These processes are carried out efficiently because living organisms can control the environment inside their bodies so that the conditions are ideal to carry out the reactions taking place. The efficient working of your body can be affected by your lifestyle and diet, by disease-causing bacteria and viruses, by smoking and by abuse of alcohol, drugs and solvents.

As this eight-week old embryo grows it will produce new cells to form tissues and organs which carry out essential life processes.

Why are there so many similarities and differences between organisms?

People often comment on how children resemble parents. 'Doesn't she have her father's eyes?' is a familiar remark. The different characteristics of humans and other animals and plants can be caused by inherited factors or by differences in the conditions in which the organism develops. Understanding how characteristics are inherited has enabled scientists to control and treat certain diseases, to develop techniques to make new and better drugs, and to breed new varieties of plants and animals to produce food.

Breeding from selected organisms has produced very useful types of plants and animals.

What do organisms need from their environment?

Green plants play a vital role in the environment; they *produce* food substances by converting carbon dioxide and water using energy from sunlight. This process, called **photosynthesis**, is the source of the energy used by all organisms in the environment. Energy is transferred from organism to organism when plants are eaten by animals which, in turn, are eaten by other animals. Plants and animals also *remove* materials from their environment for growth and other life processes. These materials are returned to the environment either in waste products or when plants and animals die and decay. In a natural environment the processes which remove materials are balanced by processes which return materials. This balance can be upset by human activity.

This land has been over-used by grazing cattle. Upsetting the natural balance in the environment can have severe and long-lasting effects.

How do human activities affect the environment?

Human activities such as building towns, quarrying and mining for materials, using land to graze animals and to grow crops, and the dumping of waste, all affect the environment around us. Environmental problems such as depletion of the ozone layer, the 'greenhouse effect', and disappearing species are regularly featured in newspapers, on TV and are now major political issues. To make decisions about how we use environmental resources we need to understand the effects of human activities. Decisions often require judging the benefit gained from products against any harmful effects on the environment. Careful management is needed to produce the food and materials we need while still protecting and caring for the environment.

Out of sight, out of mind or careful management? Difficult decisions may be needed to protect and care for the environment.

1.1 What is an environment?

Notice the difference

How would you describe the difference between sand-dunes, meadows and woodlands? There are obvious physical differences, but each area has a set of plants and animals that are suited to the conditions in that place which also contribute to the differences. The physical conditions, the plants and animals, all combine to make up the **environment** in a particular area.

Many physical factors can affect the environment – steep areas drain quickly, south facing areas are sunny. What other factors are shown here? ▼

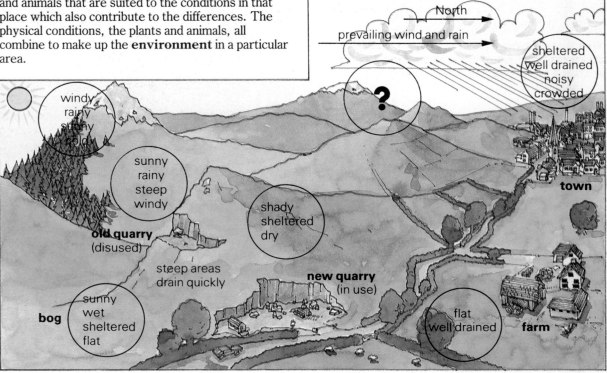

| 1 | List six conditions which you might find halfway down the highest hill shown in the picture above. |

The old quarry – an example of a habitat

The environment shown in the picture above is made up of different **habitats** – places where plants and animals live. Some habitats are natural such as moorland and bogland. Other habitats, such as quarries, farms and towns are made by people. The conditions will be different in each habitat. Temperature, pH, humidity and amount of light are conditions which will differ. The plants and animals in each habitat have features which enable them to survive in the conditions that are present in that habitat.

Because the quarry is no longer used, even larger plants have a chance to grow. ▶

Micro-habitats

There are even smaller habitats within the main habitat and these are called **micro-habitats**.

The conditions found on the underside of this overhanging rock are different to those on the side faces of the rock. Moss plants like damp conditions, so moss will grow under the rock, but not elsewhere. Only lichens can survive on the dry rock faces. Moss attracts animals such as woodlice which are also found in damp, dark places.

Together the moss and the woodlice form the **community** that lives in the micro-habitat on the underside of the rock.

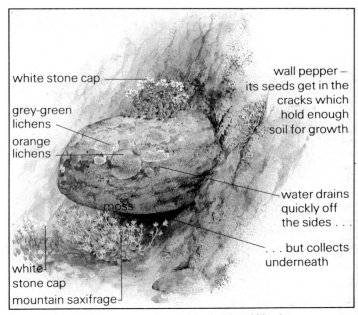

white stone cap

grey-green lichens

orange lichens

moss

wall pepper – its seeds get in the cracks which hold enough soil for growth

water drains quickly off the sides . . .

. . . but collects underneath

white stone cap

mountain saxifrage

There's a lot going on, even in a micro-habitat. Why is the saxifrage growing out from below the rock?

A perfect fit – or stuck in a rut?

Animals and plants become **adapted** to suit their habitats. Each animal and plant has to adapt to the physical conditions that exist in that habitat. Plants that develop ways of *saving water* will be able to survive in *dry* areas. Animals which develop markings that enable them to blend in with the background have less chance of being killed and eaten.

These adaptations only work as long as the plant or animal lives in its appropriate habitat. Most fish die if taken out of water; a hedgehog's spines help protect it in the wood but are no defence on the road! *If a habitat changes*, the plants and animals have to adapt quickly to the new conditions or they will die. No matter how severe the physical conditions found in any one habitat, if there is a source of food, then some animal or plant will have become adapted to live there.

This woodcock is nesting on the ground. It is well adapted – because it is very hard to see!

2 The conditions on the North side of the bush shown in the diagram opposite differ from those on the South side. The plants and animals found around the bush are suited to the conditions that are present. Study the diagram carefully and then answer the following questions:
a Where are most red dead-nettles found around the bush?
b Suggest two reasons why red dead-nettles grow better on this side?
c Give two reasons why moss only grows on the North side.
d Predict which side of the bush will contain the most animals. Explain why.

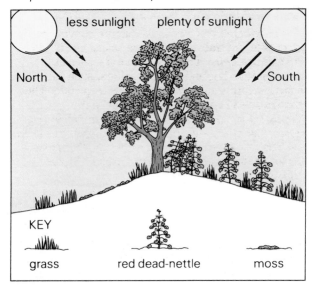

less sunlight   plenty of sunlight

North   South

KEY

grass   red dead-nettle   moss

1.2 Looking at habitats

What's the difference?

Different plants and animals are suited to different environments, but why? What sort of *factors* affect the plants? Some plants need more water than others, some need more sunlight. Some plants grow best in acid soils, and some need very little soil at all! In exploring a habitat you would have to find out these factors and their effects, but the first thing to do is to identify the plants growing in the area.

A quadrat – for surveying one area

To help count the plants in area you can use a **quadrat**. This is usually a square frame which is divided into smaller squares using string. The quadrat is placed on a piece of ground *chosen at random*. You can *either* count individual plants, *or*, if they are small, estimate the percentage of the quadrat area that each plant covers.

A transect – a wider survey

Rather than take a random sample of an area, you could use a **transect**. This is a line stretched between two pegs. You then *either* count the plants under the line *or* (more effectively) carry out a **belt transect** survey. This involves taking a series of quadrat surveys all along the length of the transect.

Whatever method you use, you should also record the physical factors at each place. For example, the depth of soil and its acidity, the percentage water content and a light reading.

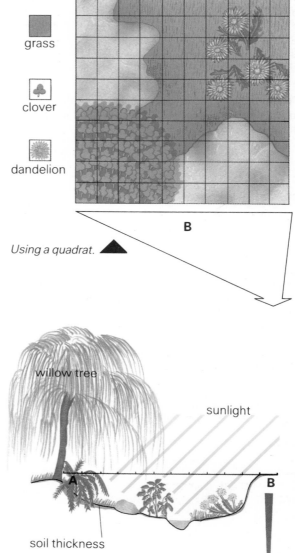

grass

clover

dandelion

Using a quadrat.

willow tree

sunlight

A

B

soil thickness

A

B

A belt transect. Each quadrat in the transect is analysed for its physical factors and plant growth.

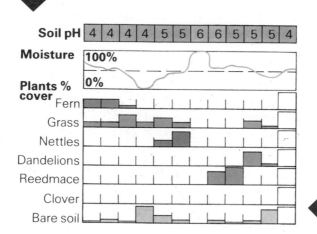

Soil pH	4	4	4	4	5	5	6	6	5	5	5	4

Moisture 100%

0%

Plants % cover

Fern

Grass

Nettles

Dandelions

Reedmace

Clover

Bare soil

---

1 From the quadrat diagram at the top of the page, estimate the percentage cover of each of the three plants shown – grass, clover and dandelions.

2 From the belt transect data shown here, identify:

 a a plant that can grow in thin soil in a sunny position?

 b the conditions in which ferns can grow?

 c the conditions needed by reedmace?

Animals on the ground

Plants are easy to count (they stay in one place) but what about moving animals? To count very small ground-living animals, you can use a jam-jar as a **pit-fall trap**. Leave the trap overnight, and then count the numbers of each type, or **species**, of animal that you have trapped. Then if you *mark* the animals you catch on the first night, and repeat the test, the numbers of *marked* animals *recaptured* will indicate the fraction of the total numbers of each species living in the area. Then you can *estimate* the total population of each species using the **Lincoln index**:

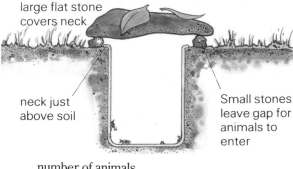

A pit-fall trap.

large flat stone covers neck

neck just above soil

Small stones leave gap for animals to enter

$$\text{Lincoln index of total population of one species} = \frac{\text{number of animals caught in first sample} \times \text{number of animals caught in second sample}}{\text{number of marked animals recaptured in second sample}}$$

How many species?

A **quadrat survey** will soon indicate the number of plant species in an area. The small animals found on trees can be collected by placing a large cloth on the ground under a branch and then **beating** the branch vigorously with a stick. Insects such as hover flies and butterflies can be caught by waving a large **sweep net** over bushes or flowers. The more species that can survive in a single habitat, the *richer* the habitat is said to be.

3 When marking animals caught in a pit-fall trap, it is best not to mark them with bright colours like yellow. Why?

4 Joan and George carry out pit-fall trap investigations in the *same* wood.

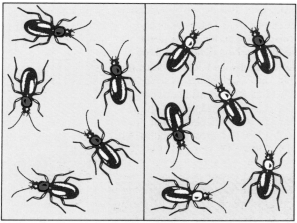

Using the Lincoln index. These samples indicate a population of (5 × 6) ÷ 2 = 15 animals of this species.

Joan's results

Trap	1st sample	2nd sample	Recaptured	Population
1	12	13	2	78
2	9	20	4	45
3	16	15	4	60
4	10	14	2	70
5	12	9	2	54

George's results

1st sample	2nd sample	Recaptured
8	12	3
15	9	4
16	15	6

a Estimate the populations for George's results.
b Which results are likely to be the most accurate? Why?
c The Lincoln index is usually only used with catches of greater than 20 animals. Why?

5 Roy and Gwillam were keen to identify the sorts of insects found around some bushes at school. They carried out separate sweeps at different times of the day. Here is a table of their results:

Sample	1	2	3	4	5	6	7
No. of species caught each sweep	26	19	28	22	24	23	21
Total number of species	26	37	42	44	45	45	46

How many different species of insect did they find? Each sweep of the bushes needed half an hour to do properly. Roy said it wasn't worth doing any more than seven samples. Do you agree? When do you think they should have given up?

7

1.3   A changing environment

Changing in time

Habitats are not fixed – they change over time. For example, quarries soon fill with soil and flowers. The changes may be caused by the weather or by plants and animals living in the community. The community itself also changes as the habitat changes.

Succession in time

If a piece of ground is cleared and then left to grow wild, at various stages different plants will grow. Each stage **succeeds** the other in time. The first group of plants that grow are called **pioneers** and these often arrive as wind-blown seeds, such as dandelion seeds. The pioneers can live on poor or thin soil. Their roots bind the soil together – preventing it from being blown away or washed away. In time, this allows plants that need better soil to become established in the area.

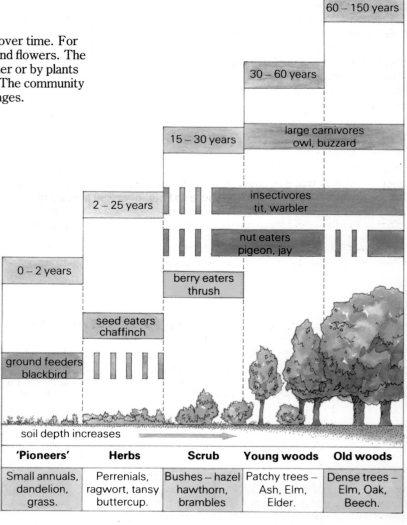

	'Pioneers'	Herbs	Scrub	Young woods	Old woods
	Small annuals, dandelion, grass.	Perrenials, ragwort, tansy buttercup.	Bushes – hazel hawthorn, brambles	Patchy trees – Ash, Elm, Elder.	Dense trees – Elm, Oak, Beech.

soil depth increases

0 – 2 years — ground feeders blackbird — seed eaters chaffinch

2 – 25 years — berry eaters thrush — nut eaters pigeon, jay

15 – 30 years — insectivores tit, warbler

30 – 60 years — large carnivores owl, buzzard

60 – 150 years

Grazing will cause a climax community to be reached early. Trees get no chance to grow in this field!

Things to note

Each stage of the succession provides *different* sorts of habitats.

The **soil** becomes deeper and richer in time due to **root action** and the build up of **dead plant material**. The deeper soil allows the larger seeds of the larger plants to grow. This allows the *number* and *variety* of plants to increase.

As the number and variety of plants increase, there is more *food* and *shelter* for animals. This means that there is an increase in the number and variety of animals.

Taller plants replace smaller ones, because the taller ones shade them and take the light.

The taller the plant, the more 'woody' it becomes. The **wood** provides the **strength** needed to **support** the plant.

Usually the last stage is dense woodland and is called the **climax community**.

Sometimes, because of the effects of climate or some other reason, the community is stopped at one of the earlier stages *before* the dense woodland. In that case the stage that is reached is called the *climax community for that habitat*.

Variety of habitats

Plants provide four main layers of habitats, each of these having its own group of insects and animals. Even though each layer tries to overshadow the ones below, they can all exist together in some places – like the edge of a wood. Sweep net catches show that different plants attract different numbers of species of insect.

tree layer

shrub layer

herb layer
ground layer

forest edge

Adapting to the habitat

When the Romans landed in Britain over two thousand years ago, they found a country that was covered with thick oak forests. Because the oak tree was so common and has been here so long, over 280 species of insect have **adapted** to living on it. Rhododendrons are not a 'native' plant of Britain – only three species of insect have had time to adapt to it.

The hawthorn tree has over 150 insect species which live on it – do you think the Hawthorn is a native tree of Britain?

Competition

In the same way that animals do, plants **compete** with each other for their food. They try to win the essential things for their growth such as space, sunlight and water. The *taller* the plant, the more sunlight it can catch. Deciduous trees have *broad* leaves which they spread so that they do not overlap each other. In doing so, they make the most of the light for themselves and also *shade* the lower plants, making it difficult for these other plants to grow.

sunlight

small tree

shadow

dandelions

nutrients

Why does the small dandelion get less light, space and nutrients from the soil?

Seasonal succession

The woodland habitats change according to the season. The cold **winter** with leafless trees is followed by **spring** with new green leaves and carpets of flowers. In **summer**, dense green foliage is followed by rich crops of fruits in the **autumn**. The russet and yellow leaves then fall to renew the leaf litter. The animals and plants in the woodland have to adapt to all these changing conditions. Some animals survive by **hibernating**. This means changing their pattern of life by having a period of limited activity. This saves energy and means they don't have to look for food when the weather is very cold.

	Feb	Mar	Apr	May	Jun	Jul	Aug	Sept	Oct
Oak					growth period				
Bluebell		growth period							

Explain why bluebells have their period of growth earlier than the oak.

1. Plants such as the daisy and plantain have flat leaves that lie close to the ground. How may that help them survive in a meadow?

2. Some trees, such as the beech, have leaves which take a long time to decay. Can you propose a theory as to why this helps the beech tree compete with other plants?

3. Describe how the appearance of a motorway embankment may change if it is not mown.

4. A student wrote 'Trees hibernate in winter by losing their leaves'. Do you agree? Explain your answer.

1.4 What is eating what?

Plants – the food producers

All living things depend eventually on plants – because plants can make food by using sunlight and simple chemicals (from the air and soil). Only green plants can make food in this way; they are called **producers**. Everything else is a **consumer**, although there are different *types* of consumers.

Herbivores are animals that eat only plants; **carnivores** are animals that eat other animals. Animals and plants that feed on dead materials are called **decomposers**.

plant (producer)

hover-fly (herbivore)

spider (carnivore)

Simple food chains are all around us. Suggest some others.

Food chains and food webs

By feeding on producers, consumers start a **food chain**. For example, an owl eats shrews that eat snails that eat plants. The carnivore consumers fit into a food chain in a certain *order*. A '**first order**' carnivore is the one which eats a herbivore; then a '**second order**' carnivore eats the 'first order' carnivore, and so on. Most carnivores eat more than one type of animal. This means that food chains link together from **food webs**.

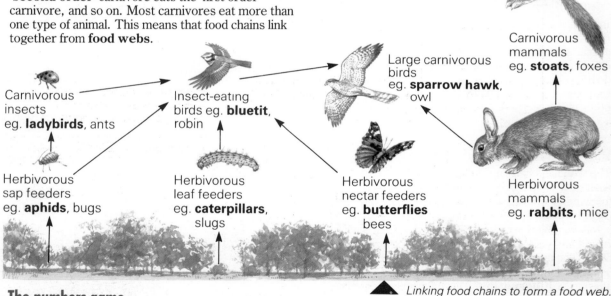

Carnivorous insects eg. **ladybirds**, ants

Insect-eating birds eg. **bluetit**, robin

Large carnivorous birds eg. **sparrow hawk**, owl

Carnivorous mammals eg. **stoats**, foxes

Herbivorous sap feeders eg. **aphids**, bugs

Herbivorous leaf feeders eg. **caterpillars**, slugs

Herbivorous nectar feeders eg. **butterflies** bees

Herbivorous mammals eg. **rabbits**, mice

Linking food chains to form a food web.

The numbers game

Suppose a ladybird eats 10 aphids a day (300 aphids a month). Ladybirds are eaten by bluetits – one bluetit might eat 10 ladybirds in a day. Each month, the bluetit will eat 300 ladybirds (which will have eaten 300 aphids each). Over 90,000 aphids have had to be eaten to keep one bluetit alive for a month!

A pyramid of numbers.

TO Sparrowhawk

2 700 000 oven ready aphids

It may be a month's food, but I don't even like aphids!

1 sparrowhawk
30 bluetits
9000 ladybirds
2 700 000 aphids

10

Pyramids of biomass

Each stage in a food chain is called a **trophic level**. A pyramid of numbers shows only the number of plants or animals at each trophic level. Usually the numbers decrease further up the pyramid, but, for example, all the aphids and ladybirds may live on just one tree! A large plant contains a lot of stored energy and this is used to support the whole pyramid of animals. The relative amount of energy stored at each level can be shown by a **pyramid of biomass** – which compares the *total mass* of plants or animals at each trophic level.

This pyramid of biomass indicates how little energy reaches the top of a food chain. ▼

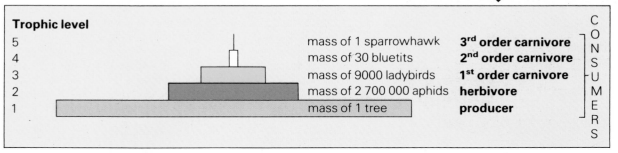

Trophic level			
5		mass of 1 sparrowhawk	**3ʳᵈ order carnivore**
4		mass of 30 bluetits	**2ⁿᵈ order carnivore**
3		mass of 9000 ladybirds	**1ˢᵗ order carnivore**
2		mass of 2 700 000 aphids	**herbivore**
1		mass of 1 tree	**producer**

CONSUMERS

Energy losses

When one animal (a predator) feeds on another (the prey), only a small amount of the energy stored in the prey passes to the predator. So food energy is *wasted* at each trophic level. This means only relatively little energy reaches the top of a food chain – so each high order carnivore needs a large food web to keep it alive.

Predator-prey cycle

In any community, the numbers of plants and animals vary because conditions change and the trophic levels **interact** with each other. This interaction is called the predator-prey cycle and is an example of **population dynamics**.

Changes in the population of the prey (or predator) disrupt the population dynamics. ▼

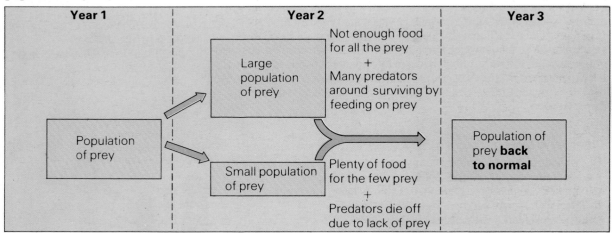

Year 1

Population of prey

Year 2

Large population of prey

Not enough food for all the prey
+
Many predators around surviving by feeding on prey

Small population of prey

Plenty of food for the few prey
+
Predators die off due to lack of prey

Year 3

Population of prey **back to normal**

1 What would happen if, one year, there were more sparrowhawks than usual?

2 Rabbits and mice can survive successfully alongside each other. Suggest a reason for this.

3 Rabbits have three large litters every year. Foxes only have a few cubs. Explain why this is so.

4 A garden is sprayed with a chemical which kills only aphids. Explain what will happen to:
   a the ladybird population;
   b the aphid and ladybird population once the chemical has been washed away by rain.

1.5 Wildlife and farming

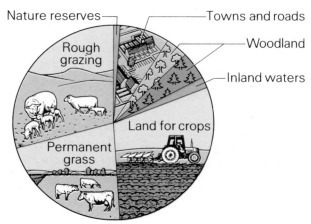

Managing the land

If you have had the chance to travel around Britain maybe you would not be surprised to learn that about 80% of the land in this country is used for agriculture. Farmers manage this land to produce vegetables, cereals or animals for human consumption and so the land is shaped to meet human needs. Farmland used to consist of a pattern of small fields, many containing different crops. In such farmland there were still a wide variety of **habitats** – hedgerows, ponds, ditches, woods and marshlands. Most wildlife survived on this managed land by seeking habitats like those found in the wild. But in recent years there have been dramatic changes.

Demand for food

The present economic situation means that farmers now have to maximise the use of their land to increase food production. It is difficult to use large machines in small fields. Since machines can't go right to the edge, a small field will have proportionally larger verges – a waste of land. So farmers have filled in ponds, grubbed out hedgerows and made their fields much larger. Farmers often specialise in a single crop, one that grows well in that area, for these large fields. This also means that expensive machinery can be used most efficiently. As a result, whole communities of flowers, shrubs and trees have been replaced by a single species. This is called **monoculture** farming.

Chemical warfare

Farmers want their chosen plant crop to grow as large as possible. Any animals, such as slugs and caterpillars, which eat the plant food are regarded as pests. Chemicals called **pesticides** are used to kill these pests. Similarly, plants which compete with the chosen crop for light and nutrients from the soil – often provided by expensive fertilisers – are killed using **herbicides**. Crops may also be treated with **fungicides** for protection against fungal diseases. Insect pests are killed with **insecticides**.

Innocent victims

The widespread use of chemical poisons in farm management was discovered – often too late – to have unexpected and disastrous effects on other wildlife. In the late 1950s, many seed-eating birds died from eating seeds treated with an insecticide called Dieldrin. A similar insecticide, called DDT, caused the death of many carnivores such as foxes, golden eagles and peregrine falcons. DDT and Dieldrin belong to a group of insecticides called **chlorinated hydrocarbons**. This group of chemicals is very damaging to wildlife because its poisonous properties have long-lasting effects. Most of them have now been withdrawn from use in the UK following public concern over their long-term persistence in the environment.

As the poison passes along the food chain it becomes more concentrated at each stage.

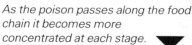

Each peregrine eats many small birds.

Each bluetit eats many aphids.

poison becomes more concentrated

crop sprayed with insecticide

Each aphid that survives contains a small quantity of insecticide.

Safer chemicals

As a result of these tragedies new types of chemical have been developed which are less hazardous to wildlife. **Organo-phosphates** and **pyrethroids** are insecticides that are far less persistent. Organophosphates have been used successfully to kill aphids feeding on crops without harming the ladybirds (which, because they eat aphids, are seen as beneficial to the farmer). However these chemicals still have to be used with care and are still likely to kill a wider range of wildlife than the target pest.

Super pests

Another problem arising from the use of chemicals is the creation of the 'super-pest'! Most insect populations contain a small number of insects that are resistant to a particular insecticide. When the insects are sprayed with the insecticide, they remain unaffected. Resistant insects are produced when insecticides are over-used. These insects breed and produce what is called a 'resistant strain' which then cannot be controlled by insecticides of the same type.

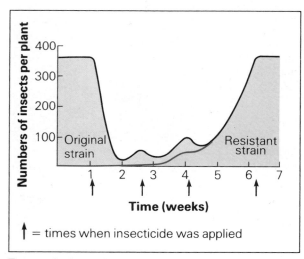

The graph shows the changing effectiveness of the use of an insecticide on an insect population.

Insecticide	LD$_{50}$ value (mg of insecticide)	Persistence
Dieldrin	40	very long-lasting
Mevinphos	3	short-lived
Resmethrin	2000	short-lived

The LD$_{50}$ test is used to measure how poisonous insecticides are. The LD$_{50}$ value is the lowest concentration of insecticide that will kill 50% of the animals treated.

Other strategies

Because of the difficulties experienced with **spraying** chemicals, other ways have been developed for controlling pests. One simple way is to breed large numbers of **predators** such as ladybirds in a laboratory and then release them into the fields that need protecting. The large number of predators quickly reduces the pest population. The predator that preys on the specific pest is specially chosen and these are called **'vectored predators'**.

Another way is to capture the males of a particular pest and **irradiate** them using a radioactive source so that they become infertile. When they are released they mate with the females but this does not produce any young. The males are captured using the scent, produced by the females of the species, called **pheromones**.

Diseases that attack a particular species can be introduced using **infected insects** and letting the disease spread through the pest population. This is a biological as compared to a chemical treatment.

---

1 The following table shows field sizes on two types of farm:

Type of farm	arable		dairy	
Date	1945	1972	1945	1972
Average field size (hectares)	8	18	3	5

   a Which type of farming needs larger fields?
   b Why do you think the field size increased between 1945 and 1972?
   c Increasing field size means removing hedges. Give three reasons why this reduces wildlife.

2 From the table of insecticides above decide
   a which insecticide is the most poisonous?
   b which is likely to harm other wildlife the least? (Give two reasons for your choice.)
   c which insecticide would you use to treat seeds so that they are not eaten by pests in the ground before they are able to grow.

3 Use the graph to answer the following.
   a Why do most insects die after the first spraying?
   b Explain why the numbers rise again after the third spraying.
   c Explain what you think is happening between the 2nd and the 5th weeks.

Harvests from the wild

Meeting food demands

Modern farming methods have increased the amount and variety of foods that you can buy from shops and supermarkets. Large areas of the countryside are used by farmers to grow plant crops such as potatoes and wheat and to raise animals such as cattle and sheep. Even so animals from natural habitats are used as a food resource. Whales, deer, geese, fish and shellfish are examples of animals which are harvested from their natural habitats.

Whales have been used as a source of food and materials for centuries.

Over-exploited

Blue whales have been harvested for many years and used as a source of food and materials. The use of large whaling fleets, particularly by Japan and Russia, meant that large numbers were killed each year. The number of blue whales in the seas and oceans decreased year after year and the species faced complete extinction unless their removal was controlled. Over-exploitation of blue whales shows that if animals are killed more quickly than they can reproduce their numbers will decline.

Another example of over-exploitation is the fishing for anchovy around the coast of Peru. The large numbers of anchovies made this area the world's most productive fishing region. Many hundreds of tonnes of anchovies were harvested each year from 1960 to 1972. Eventually catches became very poor because there were fewer and fewer fish remaining. Over-fishing in this region removed fish more quickly than they could reproduce and so their numbers steadily declined.

Over 10 million tonnes of anchovy were caught each year in the 1960s.

Effects of over-fishing

Fish in the seas around Britain have also been affected by over-fishing. Cod, herring and plaice are popular sources of food and trawlers have been catching large quantities of these fish for many years. The graph opposite shows the amount of plaice caught over a number of years. What can we learn from this data to help us control the size of fish populations?

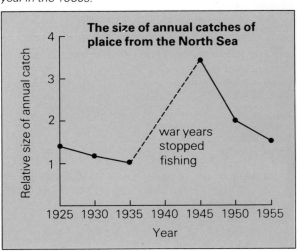

The size of annual catches of plaice from the North Sea

war years stopped fishing

Managing wild populations

Animals from natural environments can be used as a source of food. To avoid over-exploitation it is necessary to control the numbers of animals removed from the wild population. This is achieved by:

- setting **quotas** – regulating the maximum size of a catch or the number of animals that can be removed;
- allowing animals to reproduce by preventing the removal of animals during their **breeding season** or by avoiding their **breeding areas**;
- allowing only animals of a certain size of age to be caught so that smaller or younger animals can grow and reproduce.

Farming the seas

Most land animals that are used as a source of food are reared as domesticated farm animals. This involves using selected breeds, providing the right foods and controlling pests and predators. Similar farming methods are now being used to increase the production of food from the sea. The populations of fish are 'farmed' by removing predators and controlling disease, breeding better types, and by controlling environmental conditions to promote growth. Farming methods on land have created artificial environments which are very different to natural habitats. Farming the sea also involves creating artificial marine environments in order to increase food production.

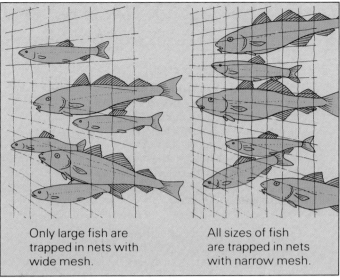

Only large fish are trapped in nets with wide mesh.

All sizes of fish are trapped in nets with narrow mesh.

Controlling the mesh size of fishing nets helps to maintain fish stocks.

Fish farms create an artificial environment.

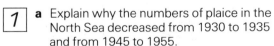

1
  a Explain why the numbers of plaice in the North Sea decreased from 1930 to 1935 and from 1945 to 1955.
  b Why did the numbers of plaice rise in 1945?

2 Explain why catches of anchovies became steadily worse between 1972 and 1980 even though fishermen tried harder and harder to catch fish.

3 There are regulations which control the size of the mesh of fishing nets.

Explain why regulating mesh size helps to control the size of fish population.

1.7 Polluting our environment

Polluting the air . . . . .

Air pollution has increased greatly since the widespread use of fossil fuels in the home, in industry and in motor cars. Nearly a billion tonnes of fossil fuel is burnt every year. Although most of the gases are invisible they can cause great damage to plants, people and the environment generally.

Fossil fuels like coal, oil and petrol all produce pollutants when burnt, as do other industries such as chemical and cement works.

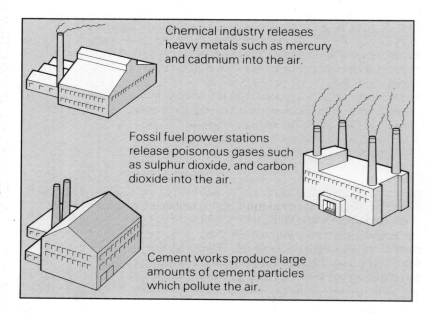

Chemical industry releases heavy metals such as mercury and cadmium into the air.

Fossil fuel power stations release poisonous gases such as sulphur dioxide, and carbon dioxide into the air.

Cement works produce large amounts of cement particles which pollute the air.

. . . with acid rain

The pollutant gases, sulphur dioxide and nitrogen dioxide, when released into the air dissolve in the rain to form weak **acid rain**. The acid rain eats away stone and many historic buildings, like cathedrals, have been badly damaged. It also pollutes rivers poisoning river life. The acid rain can fall many hundreds of miles away from where it was formed. The acid rain formed in Britain can fall in Sweden or Denmark, for example, and so causes international problems.

$$S + O_2 \longrightarrow SO_2 + water \longrightarrow sulphuric\ (iv)\ acid$$
$$N + O_2 \longrightarrow NO_2 + water \longrightarrow nitric\ (v)\ acid$$

The chemical reactions that take place causing the formation of weak acid pollutants.

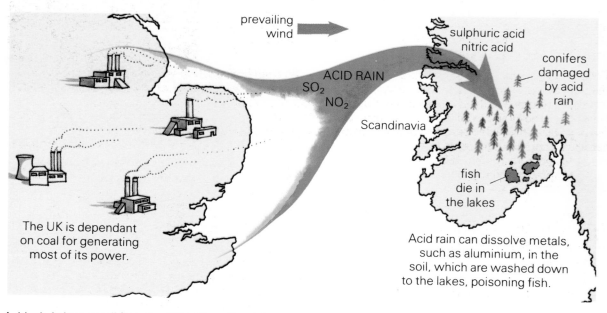

prevailing wind

sulphuric acid
nitric acid

ACID RAIN
SO_2
NO_2

conifers damaged by acid rain

Scandinavia

fish die in the lakes

The UK is dependant on coal for generating most of its power.

Acid rain can dissolve metals, such as aluminium, in the soil, which are washed down to the lakes, poisoning fish.

Acid rain is 'exported' from the UK to Scandinavia!

.... with smoke and smog

Not all pollution is invisible. **Smoke** is made of tiny particles of carbon floating in the air which can be seen. These particles can damage the delicate tissues in the lungs. They also scatter sunlight, reducing the amount available for photosynthesis. The effects of smoke are made worse when the conditions for forming a fog exist. The water then condenses on the smoke particles making a dirty fog called a '**smog**'. As a result of the severe smog in London in 1952, the Clean Air Act of 1956 was passed. This created smokeless zones where coal could not be burnt – only 'smokeless' fuels. This Act, together with the move to nuclear power stations, has resulted in the air being much cleaner. The invisible pollutants, however, have continued to increase.

.... with carbon monoxide and lead

One of the waste products when petrol is burnt in a car engine is carbon monoxide. The number of cars increases every year making this a major source of pollution. **Carbon monoxide** combines irreversibly with a chemical in the blood called haemoglobin – preventing the blood from carrying oxygen round the body efficiently. A running car engine in a closed space could cause a person's blood to become so contaminated that death follows. Cigarettes also produce carbon monoxide and as much as 10% of a smoker's blood may be affected.

Lead is added to petrol to ensure that it burns smoothly. This lead is passed into the air as very fine particles in the exhaust gases. If lead is breathed in it can cause problems with our nervous and digestive systems. Young children are particularly vunerable to lead poisoning and high concentrations can lead to brain damage. **Lead-free petrol** is now being sold to protect the environment from lead pollution.

Polluting the water

Water is often used in industrial processes and many factories are placed close to rivers so that water is available. Often this water can become contaminated with a variety of chemicals. A few years ago, someone developed a photographic film in water taken from the mouth of the river Rhine, using no other chemicals than those that were already in the water, just to prove how polluted that river is! Chemicals such as **mercury** can get into the food chain often through contaminated fish and shellfish. Mercury in contaminated fish can cause serious damage to the nervous system of anyone eating the fish.

Pollution may be thought of as any product of human activity that upsets the natural state of affairs. The water used in the cooling towers of power stations is returned to the river at a *higher temperature* and so can also be considered a pollutant, even though it is clean. This warmer water *increases the activity* of bacteria and they use up more oxygen, making it harder for large animals to survive.

We are even polluting the upper levels of our atmosphere. Chemicals from aerosol cans – chlorofluorocarbons (CFCs) – break down the ozone layer which protects us from the sun's radiation.

| 1 | What evidence is there that air polution damages the environment? |

| 3 | Explain how carbon monoxide can kill. |

| 2 | Plants in smoky areas do not photosynthesise as much as plants in smoke free zones. Can you suggest two reasons why? |

| 4 | Considering the pollution caused by the car and the high number of people killed and injured on the roads do you think there should be a 'Ban the Car' movement? Discuss this in your group. |

1.8 Disappearing wildlife

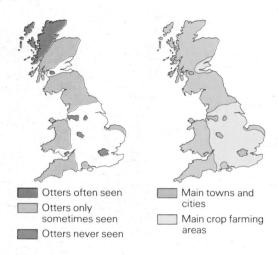

Otters often seen
Otters only sometimes seen
Otters never seen
Main towns and cities
Main crop farming areas

The map on the left shows the distribution of otters. The other map shows the main crop-farming areas.

The disappearing otter

From 1977 to 1979 a survey was carried out to find out how many otters there were in different parts of the country. The results are shown on the map opposite.

Otters used to be a fairly common sight in many areas of Britain. Their numbers declined in the late 1950s and early 1960s. The decline was unusual because it happened at about the same time across certain parts of the country. Some people claimed that the main crop farming areas were the worst affected. Look at both the maps. Do you agree?

The first map shows that otters are now totally absent or very rare in most regions. Only in the remote parts of Scotland has the otter population remained at a high level. This suggests that human activity may have caused the decline in the otter population.

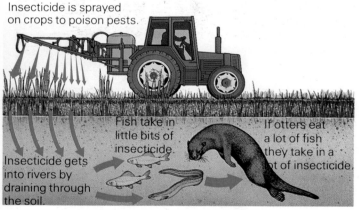

Insecticide is sprayed on crops to poison pests.

Insecticide gets into rivers by draining through the soil.

Fish take in little bits of insecticide.

If otters eat a lot of fish they take in a lot of insecticide.

A case of food poisoning

There are a number of ways that human activity could affect otters. The most likely is the use of chemical poisons called **insecticides** that are used to kill insect pests. It was in the early 1950s that insecticides called organochlorides were first widely used by farmers to kill insect pests. These chemicals were soon washed into rivers and lakes. This diagram shows you the effect these poisons have on the life of the river.

Food chains – a fatal link?

The effect of chemical poisons like organochlorides is often only seen in the final link in a food chain. The concentration of insecticide in the water may not be high enough to kill fish. But over the years, it does poison carnivores such as the otter. Birds like herons and grebes are also affected.

Just how does the insecticide become more deadly as it passes along the food chain? This diagram shows how even a little insecticide can harm the otter.

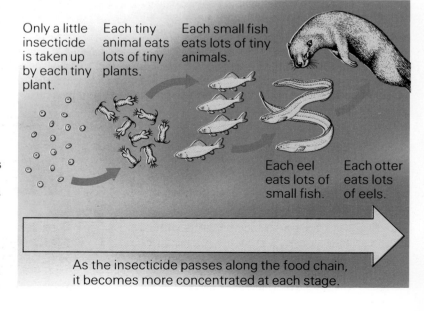

Only a little insecticide is taken up by each tiny plant.

Each tiny animal eats lots of tiny plants.

Each small fish eats lots of tiny animals.

Each eel eats lots of small fish.

Each otter eats lots of eels.

As the insecticide passes along the food chain, it becomes more concentrated at each stage.

Disappearing owls

In 1935 it was estimated that there were more than 12 000 pairs of barn owls breeding in England and Wales. By 1985 the number of barn owls had been reduced to only 3778 breeding pairs. A drop of over 50% in the last 50 years.

The life of a barn owl

Barn owls are very efficient hunters of mice and other small mammals that can be found in unploughed fields and in hedgerows. Snow covered fields can hide the owl's prey during winter months. Nesting usually starts in February or March and eggs are laid in early May. Only the female owl incubates the eggs and she hardly ever leaves the nest during the four to five weeks it takes for the eggs to hatch. Soon after the eggs are hatched the female bird leaves the nest and flies to the nearest water to bathe herself. They often choose steep-sided cattle troughs which can be found at the side of fields.

Cause of owl deaths

Scientists carried out an investigation to find out whether the population decline of barn owls was due to natural causes or due to the impact of human activity. The different causes of death are shown in the graphs below. Use this information to answer the questions which follow.

This young owl will have to live through many hazards before it will breed.

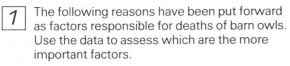

1 The following reasons have been put forward as factors responsible for deaths of barn owls. Use the data to assess which are the more important factors.

Use of pesticides by farmers.
Removal of hedgerows.
Increase in number of cars and roads.

2 a State a difference between the deaths of male and female owls.
   b Suggest a possible reason for this difference.

3 It takes a high concentration of insecticide to kill an otter. Explain why otters can take in a high enough dose of insecticide to kill them even though they do not eat insects.

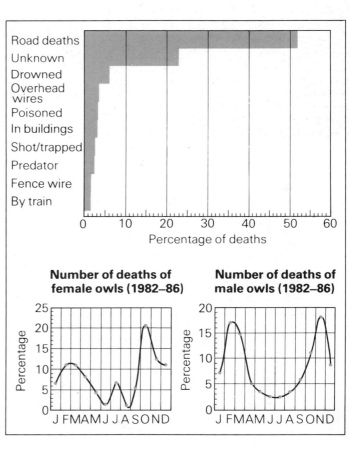

1.9   A threat to habitats

Destruction of habitats

Vast numbers of plants and animals are disappearing from many parts of the world. Many are **endangered species** that may soon be completely extinct. Farming, mining, forestry and the building of roads, reservoirs and homes – all of these have led to the destruction of many habitats. Pollution threatens those plants and animals that manage to survive. Britain has several endangered species. To help these species survive, scientists need to study all the environmental factors affecting that species.

A toad in a hole!

There are only two species of toad native to Britain, the natterjack and the common toads. Natterjacks are now an endangered species. What environmental factors have brought this about? To answer this question, we must look at its habitat.

Natterjack habitat

The ideal habitat for a natterjack toad is open, sunny, warm, sandy soil where it can easily burrow for food. It also needs shallow pools for breeding. These conditions can be found in heathland or in sand dunes. The natterjack is common in Mediterranean countries but Britain is at the northern limit of its range. This explains why even slight changes in the habitat could make Britain unsuitable for natterjack toads.

Heathland habitat

Heathland is a special type of climax community – grazing (or fire) has stopped the habitat from becoming woodland. The amount of grazing has decreased in recent years. As a result, trees and shrubs have begun to grow on heathland. These plants create shade, and so cool the soil and any pools of water. Trees can reduce the temperature of exposed soil from 37°C down to 14°C. These conditions do not suit the natterjack, but are just right for the common toad.

Competition

The common toad will die if the sun dries it out (dessication). Normally the common toad is not found on heathlands because this habitat does not provide enough shade. When the heathlands were open sandy heaths, the natterjack alone lived in this habitat. Now that the trees are shading the heath, the common toads live in the same habitats as the natterjack.

The amount of trees in a habitat effects the population of the natterjack and the common toads – but in different ways!

The natterjack toad – threatened!

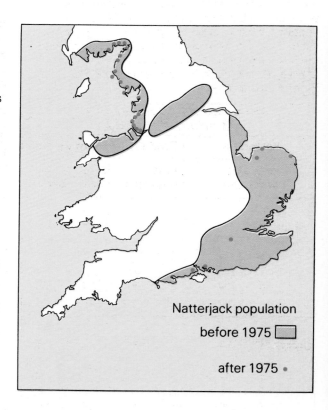

Natterjack population

before 1975 ☐

after 1975 •

Tree cover	Numbers of toads found	
	Natterjack	**Common**
Light	2	0
Medium	5	60
Heavy	13	92

The common toad eats the same food as the natterjack and so is in direct competition with it. Even worse, since the natterjack tends to breed later than the common toads, the common toad tadpoles are big enough to eat the natterjack tadpoles as soon as they hatch – deadly competition indeed!

Dune habitat

Sand dunes provide an alternative habitat for natterjack toads. Hollows in the sand form shallow pools, called **slacks** which are used by the natterjack for breeding. Although it is an ideal habitat, it may also may be a fatally temporary one. The wind may blow sand to fill in the pool, or it may just dry out – killing the natterjack toad and any of its eggs or tadpoles. Sometimes dune habitats have been drained to provide caravan sites.

Digging for survival

To help the natterjack survive in the dune habitat, special pools called **scrapes** were dug. These pools were deep enough so as to prevent filling in or drying out. The scrapes were designed to increase the population of the natterjacks. For in the first two years after they had been dug, the survival rate was about 25%. The project seems to be working. Then the following figures were obtained.

■ Why do you think the scrapes became less effective with time? ▼

Comparison of slacks and scrapes (3 years after digging)			
Natterjack	**Predators caught in pool**		
tadpoles surviving	Water boatman	Water spider	Diving beetle
Slack A 7%	3	13	144
B 28%	0	0	4
C 1%	9	6	185
Scrape D 0%	39	18	295
E 0%	127	24	238
F 0%	53	27	136

A typical natterjack habitat.

The secret of surviving

By looking at the table below you can see that the factors affecting the survival of a species are complex and varied. Probably no single factor is responsible, but all of them play their part. The effects of human activity on the habitats play a major part – whether stopping grazing on heathland or starting up holiday camps. On a much larger scale it is our actions, both individually and as a society, that pose the greatest threat to the many environments all over the Earth. Only by using our knowledge of environments, and by educating everyone to be aware of their effect on their environment, will it be possible to save our world which is under threat in so many ways?

Sample of natterjack habitats (1983)		
	Heathland	**Dunes**
Eggs		
– failed to hatch	14%	7%
– dried out	28%	5%
– swamped by tide	–	1%
– eaten by predators	2%	2%
– hatched as tadpoles	56%	85%
Tadpoles		
– died by drying out	1%	33%
– died during growth	1%	2%
– total surviving	54%	50%

1 Far less tadpoles hatch in the heathland pools than in the dune sites. What may cause this?

2 What problems do you think would face the common toad in Spain?

3 The smooth snake is another endangered species. Prepare an informative notice explaining to reptile collectors why they should not remove it from its habitat.

1.10 *Life on Earth*

The biosphere

All life on Earth lives in a thin 'shell' of the Earth's crust that rises 5000 m above sea-level and falls to about 8000 m below sea-level. This band is called the **biosphere**. Most animals and plants live in an even thinner band that only reaches 1000 m above and 1000 m below sea-level. Beyond these limits, the physical conditions make it difficult for life to exist.

Why is there life on Earth?

Life on Earth developed in the water of the oceans millions of years ago. Water is essential for life, as we know it. But water is only in its liquid state over a small range of temperature – 0°C to 100°C. The 'normal' atmospheric temperatures of planets closer to or further away from the Sun are well outside this range and so, because there is no water on these planets, they are not likely to support the forms of life found on Earth.

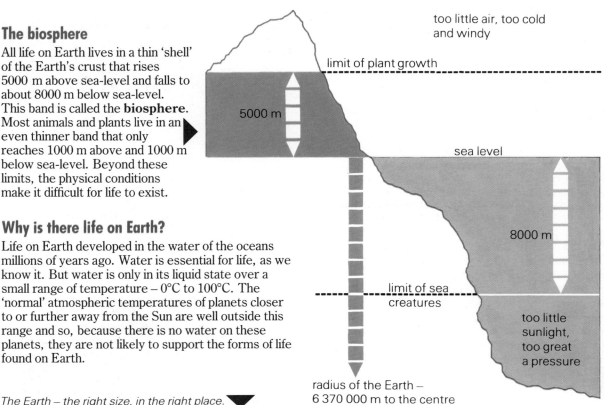

too little air, too cold and windy

limit of plant growth

5000 m

sea level

8000 m

limit of sea creatures

too little sunlight, too great a pressure

radius of the Earth – 6 370 000 m to the centre

The Earth – the right size, in the right place. ▼

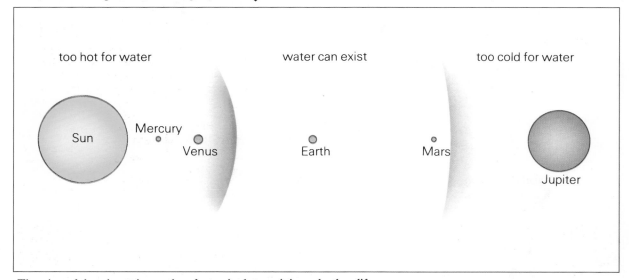

too hot for water

water can exist

too cold for water

Sun

Mercury

Venus

Earth

Mars

Jupiter

The size of the planet is another factor in determining whether life can exist. Planets larger than the Earth have hydrogen-rich atmospheres. Planets smaller than Earth are too small to hold any atmosphere. Earth is large enough to hold an atmosphere, yet small enough to allow hydrogen to 'leak' away making the atmosphere **oxygen-rich** – another essential for life. So you can see that the Earth is rare amongst planets in having a biosphere which allows for the rich variety of life we take for granted. But the thin shell of the biosphere, home for millions of living things, is itself fragile and can be upset by human interference.

The hottest topic on Earth

Plants and animals are continually exchanging materials and energy with their non-living surroundings. They interact with each other to form a complex network of activity – **the environment**. Gases in the atmosphere are normally stable because there is a balance in their production and removal. But lately this balance has been disturbed by human activity. The large scale **burning of fossil fuels** and the world-wide **destruction of forests** has led to an increase in the amount of carbon dioxide in the Earth's atmosphere. Scientists believe that the build up of these gases is causing a **'greenhouse'** effect leading to an increase in the Earth's temperature.

The greenhouse effect

Light from the sun is rich in short wavelength (high energy) light which can pass through the gases in the atmosphere and be absorbed by the Earth, making it warmer. Much of the heat is then radiated back into space, but at longer wavelengths (low energy). Gases, especially carbon dioxide, in the atmosphere absorb this light, trapping its heat and so act as a sort of blanket. Without this blanket the Earth would be a frozen, lifeless planet. . . . but the build-up of too much carbon dioxide in the atmosphere is beginning to make the blanket too hot for comfort!

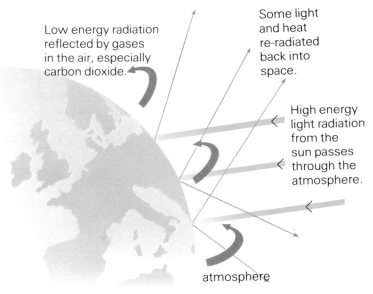

Low energy radiation reflected by gases in the air, especially carbon dioxide.

Some light and heat re-radiated back into space.

High energy light radiation from the sun passes through the atmosphere.

atmosphere

The build-up of carbon dioxide prevents low energy radiation from escaping into space – and the Earth heats up.

Upsetting the balance

The energy the Earth receives each year from the sun is balanced by the heat energy lost to outer space. This is just one example of the many ways in which our environment on Earth is finely balanced. The greenhouse effect shows how humans can upset this delicate balance and create great environmental problems. We all depend on the environment for food, oxygen and fuel. We should increase our understanding of the environment in which we all live so that we can gain useful knowledge and lessen the damage we cause. This is important for all animals and plants that live on this planet – including you.

Pollution threatens to scorch the Earth

Michael White in Washington and Tim Rudford

As the United States buckles under the impact of the worst drought in 50 years, American scientists have confirmed that man-made pollutants are finally beginning to produce the long-predicted and potentially disastrous "greenhouse effect" on the earth's climate.

Dr James Hansen, the director of Nasa's Institute for Space Studies and an expert on climate, told a Senate committee on the drought: "It's time to stop waffling so much and say the evidence is pretty strong that the greenhouse effect is here."

The four warmest years in the past 100 have been in the 1980s. And as he spoke, agricultural experts warned that the world food stockpile could shrink to dangerously low levels over the next year, as the US grain-belt, in effect the food basket of the world, shrivels in the record temperatures.

Daily Telegraph, June '88

The recent droughts in the USA ruined crops. This may be one of the results of the greenhouse effect.

2.1 *Plants – the food producers*

Using solar energy

Plants are called **producers** because they are able to make their own food from simple raw materials around them by a process called **photosynthesis**. During this process plants use the energy in sunlight to convert carbon dioxide and water into sugars. Oxygen is produced as a by-product of the process. The energy in sunlight is absorbed by **chlorophyll** – a green substance found in the leaves of plants. During photosynthesis the energy from sunlight becomes 'trapped' as chemical energy in the sugars that are produced.

The energy factory

The reactions which convert carbon dioxide and water into sugars take place in the **chloroplasts** of leaf cells. The diagrams below show how the design of leaves makes them highly efficient 'factories' of photosynthesis.

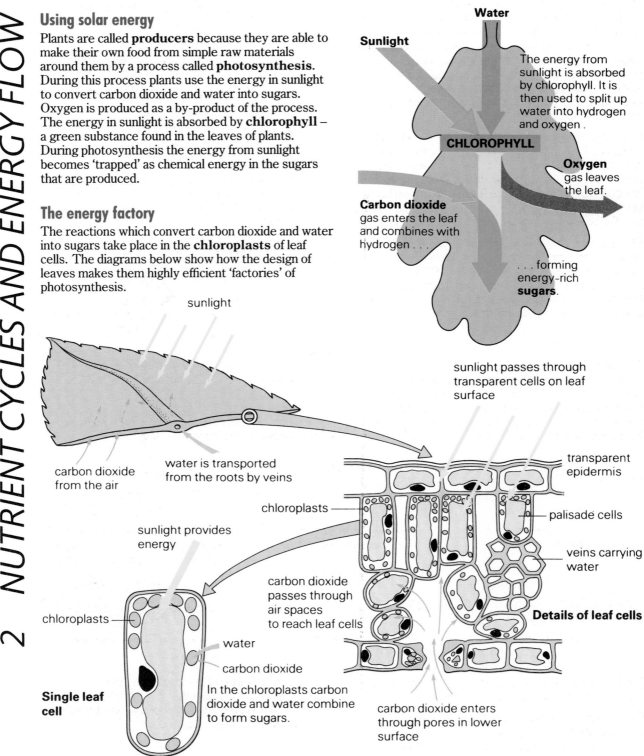

Water

Sunlight

The energy from sunlight is absorbed by chlorophyll. It is then used to split up water into hydrogen and oxygen .

CHLOROPHYLL

Oxygen gas leaves the leaf.

Carbon dioxide gas enters the leaf and combines with hydrogen . . .

. . . forming energy-rich **sugars**.

sunlight

carbon dioxide from the air

water is transported from the roots by veins

sunlight passes through transparent cells on leaf surface

chloroplasts

sunlight provides energy

carbon dioxide passes through air spaces to reach leaf cells

chloroplasts

water

carbon dioxide

transparent epidermis

palisade cells

veins carrying water

Details of leaf cells

Single leaf cell

In the chloroplasts carbon dioxide and water combine to form sugars.

carbon dioxide enters through pores in lower surface

Leaves are specially adapted to get light, water and carbon dioxide directly to the chloroplasts – to produce sugars and oxygen.

24

What happens to the sugars?

Photosynthesis can *only* take place in those parts of the plant that contain chlorophyll. Since most of the chlorophyll is found in the leaves, most of the food is made there. But the food is needed by every part of the plant, so the sugars dissolve in water and are carried round to all parts of the plant. Once there, the sugars provide the energy for processes such as growth. If the energy is not used straight away, the sugars are changed into more complex **carbohydrates** such as starch and cellulose, which are *not* soluble in water.

Plant food is stored as starch, because the **starch** can be turned back into sugar again later on and *used for energy*. **Cellulose** is added to various parts of the plant to make them *stiff and strong*. Once the sugar has been made into cellulose it can't be turned back into sugar. Cellulose is the part that forms the fibre in our diet when we eat plant matter.

Plants make other foods, such as proteins, as well as sugars. Through their roots, they can take in **nitrates** dissolved in the soil water. Nitrogen in the nitrates is used along with carbon, oxygen and hydrogen to make the **proteins** used in making the new cells needed for plant growth.

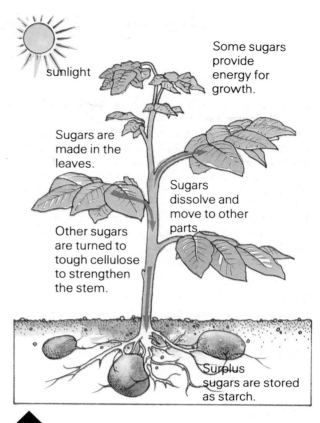

Some sugars provide energy for growth.

Sugars are made in the leaves.

Sugars dissolve and move to other parts.

Other sugars are turned to tough cellulose to strengthen the stem.

sunlight

Surplus sugars are stored as starch.

The sugars produced in photosynthesis are dissolved and pass round the plant to where they are needed.

Testing that starch is made in sunlight

The sugars made in a leaf during photosynthesis may be stored there for a short time. The presence of such starch is easy to test since starch turns orange-brown **iodine** solution, blue-black. Winston and Carol used this test to look for the presence of starch in leaves kept under different conditions:

What do these results show about the conditions needed for photosynthesis?

samples

leaf 1

Leaf from a plant kept in the dark for 1 day.

leaf 2

Leaf from a plant kept in the dark for 3 days

leaf 3

Leaf from a plant kept as leaf 2 then taken back into the light after covering with an L–shape

Test results

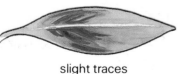

slight traces

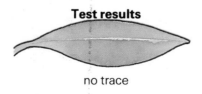

no trace

strong reaction except for covered area

1 State three ways the leaves on a tree are able to trap as much sunlight as possible.

2 Look at the diagram of the structure of a leaf on the opposite page.
  a Why is the epidermis on top of the leaf clear?
  b Why are more chloroplasts found near the top of the pallisade cells?

3 Carol says the group need a 'control' experiment to make their test fair. What 'control' would you suggest and what results would you expect it to show?

25

2.2 Capturing the Sun's energy

Energy for all living things

The Sun is the source of energy for *all* forms of life. Plants use the Sun directly to make their food. Animals use it indirectly, getting their energy by eating plants or herbivores. Green plants use the energy in sunlight and convert it into sugars – which can then be used to store chemical energy in food substances, such as starch. This process of **photosynthesis** is the key to the whole food chain of life. So let's look at what plants need to photosynthesise.

Investigating photosynthesis ...

A group of students thought that the following 'ingredients' were needed for photosynthesis:
● light ● carbon dioxide ● chlorophyll – the green pigment in plants

■ Do you agree with their list? What else do you think might be needed?

The students investigated their hypothesis by removing each of the three factors from three different leaves of the same plant. They then tested each of the three leaves for the presence of starch to determine if photosynthesis had taken place.

First they chose a plant which had *variegated* (different coloured) leaves. The absence of a green colour indicates that there is no chlorophyll in that part of the leaf (e.g. Leaf 1). They then put the plant into a cupboard for two days. One of the leaves was covered with aluminium foil (to block out the light) and another was placed in a flask containing soda-lime (a chemical which absorbs carbon dioxide). The plant was left in bright sunshine for 24 hours. The diagram shows the results the students obtained when they tested the three leaves for starch.

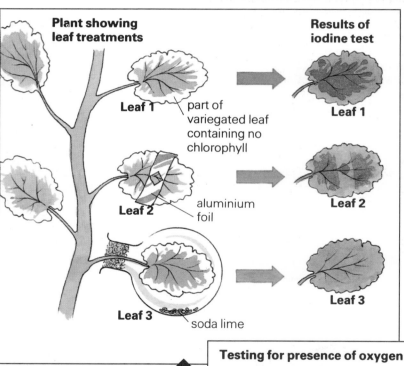

Plant showing leaf treatments

Results of iodine test

Leaf 1 — part of variegated leaf containing no chlorophyll

Leaf 2 — aluminium foil

Leaf 3 — soda lime

Each of the three differently treated leaves were tested with iodine solution to see if starch had been produced. What do you think these results show?

The students then tested to see if oxygen is given off during photosynthesis. How would you make sure this test was fair?

... and its products

The students then began to wonder what other things might be made during photosynthesis, besides sugars for food. They already knew that *oxygen* and *carbon dioxide* are exchanged during respiration – so they wondered if these two gases might be exchanged *in reverse* during photosynthesis. They decided to test if oxygen is given off from plants during photosynthesis.

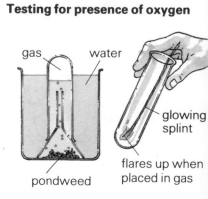

Testing for presence of oxygen

gas   water

glowing splint

flares up when placed in gas

pondweed

Simple ... isn't it?

The students were able to conclude from these, and other, investigations that **carbon dioxide** and **water** are the *raw materials* of photosynthesis, **sugars** and **oxygen** are the *products*; **light energy** and **chlorophyll** are *also* needed for the process to take place. But the process is quite complex – the plant is a bit like a tiny chemical factory!

Chlorophyll is present in the **chloroplasts** of leaf cells. The chloroplasts absorb energy from sunlight and use it to split the molecules of water (taken in by the plant) into oxygen and hydrogen. Oxygen is lost as a by-product and hydrogen is added to carbon dioxide (taken in from the air) to form glucose and other sugars. *Adding hydrogen* to (or *removing oxygen* from) a chemical is called **reduction**. So during photosynthesis, we can say that *carbon dioxide is reduced to form glucose*. This is not a simple reaction – it involves many stages, each requiring a special enzyme, before carbon dioxide and water can be transformed into useful sugars.

PHOTOSYNTHESIS

WATER + CARBON DIOXIDE

① **Chloroplasts** absorb **sunlight energy**

② Chloroplasts use energy from sunlight to *remove hydrogen* from water

③ Oxygen produced when hydrogen removed from water

④ Enzymes *add hydrogen* (from water) to carbon dioxide, forming glucose (by a chemical reduction)

OXYGEN + GLUCOSE

Building up stores

Some of the glucose produced by photosynthesis will break down right away to release its stored energy. The process of *releasing* stored energy is called **respiration**. The rest of the glucose is turned into starch and stored. To form starch, individual glucose molecules react together (in the presence of enzymes) to form a long chain molecule. Any molecule made up of a series of repeated units is called a **polymer**. Starch is a polymer containing hundreds of glucose units.

Some plants store starch in the cells of leaves, stems or roots. Other plants have special storage organs. For example, the potato tuber is a storage organ which holds large reserves of starch. The plant can turn starch back into glucose when it is needed.

Plants also use glucose to make another polymer called **cellulose**. Cellulose is needed to make the cell walls of a plant. The plant cannot turn cellulose back into glucose, so it cannot be used as a storage substance.

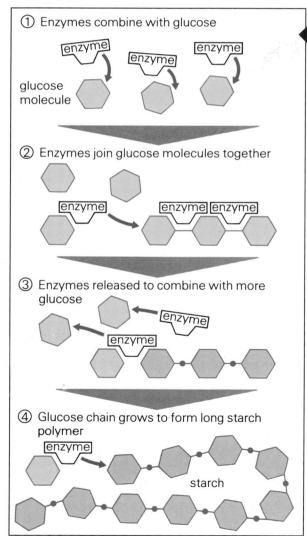

① Enzymes combine with glucose

glucose molecule

② Enzymes join glucose molecules together

③ Enzymes released to combine with more glucose

④ Glucose chain grows to form long starch polymer

starch

---

1 Explain how light energy is used during photosynthesis.

2 Explain how you would use iodine to test a leaf for starch.

3 **a** Make a large copy of the table below. Use the headings to show the students' observations and the interpretation of the results of their first investigation.

Leaf treatment	Diagram of leaf after starch test	Interpretation of results

b Why did the students use a plant which had been kept in a dark cupboard for two days?

2.3　*Bigger and better crops*

Measuring the rate of photosynthesis

A group of students carried out an investigation to find out how photosynthesis is affected by changing certain conditions. They measured the rate of photosynthesis by counting the number of bubbles produced each minute by an aquatic plant called *Elodea*. They each used a 4 cm length of *Elodea*.

Leroy carried out his investigation near the window.

Peter worked in the middle of the room using a lamp as a source of light.

Lisa placed aluminium foil around the tube containing the plant.

The results of their investigations are shown in the table opposite.

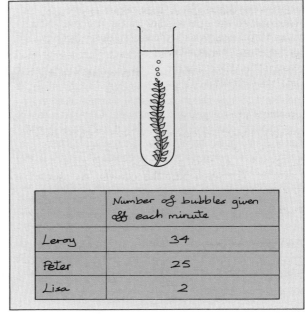

	Number of bubbles given off each minute
Leroy	34
Peter	25
Lisa	2

Measuring the rate of photosynthesis.

1　**a** Why is the number of bubbles produced different for each student?
　　b Name the gas in the bubbles.
　　c Why did the students use the same length of *Elodea*?

Extending the investigation

Peter noticed that the tube he was using became warm during the investigation. The group decided to change the design of their apparatus and to repeat the investigation at two different temperatures. They also decided to control the amount of light by changing the distance from the lamp to the beaker.

Their results are shown in the table opposite.

2　**a** Why did the students place the tube containing *Elodea* in a beaker of water?
　　b The students concluded that the rate of photosynthesis is increased by increasing the amount of light and increasing temperature. Do you agree with their conclusion? Explain your answer.

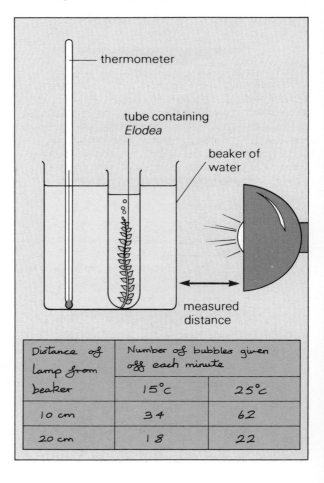

Distance of lamp from beaker	Number of bubbles given off each minute	
	15°C	25°C
10 cm	34	62
20 cm	18	22

Making the most of sunshine

Plant growers try to improve the yields of their crops by providing ideal growing conditions. A very common way of doing this is by using a greenhouse. The conditions inside a greenhouse allow plants to be grown earlier in the year and in regions where they would not normally grow. The temperature in a greenhouse is normally much higher than the outside temperature because they retain the heat generated by the Sun's rays.

Improving conditions

Many commercial growers use greenhouses which are heated during cold weather. Some use electricity to provide heat while others burn fuels such as paraffin. When fuels burn the following reaction takes place:

fuel + oxygen $\longrightarrow$ carbon dioxide + water + heat energy

The diagram opposite shows the same type of tomatoes grown in an unheated greenhouse and in a greenhouse heated by burning paraffin. Both greenhouses received the same amount of sunlight.

3 **a** Which greenhouse produced the highest yield?
   b Give two reasons why the yield was different.

Better lighting

Artificial lighting can be used to grow plants when the amount of sunlight falls too low. However, very few growers use artificial lighting and rely on sunlight as the only source of energy. The bar chart below shows the amount of sunlight entering greenhouses in southern and northern England throughout the year. The chart also shows the amount of light needed to grow chrysanthemums.

4 **a** During which months would you advise chrysanthemum growers in the South of England to use artificial lighting?
   b Why do chrysanthemums not grow well in January even when the greenhouse is heated?

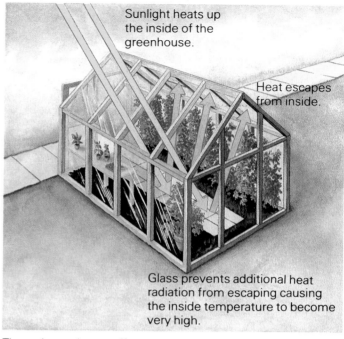

Sunlight heats up the inside of the greenhouse.

Heat escapes from inside.

Glass prevents additional heat radiation from escaping causing the inside temperature to become very high.

The real greenhouse effect.

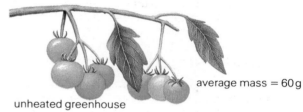

average mass = 60 g

unheated greenhouse

average mass = 85 g

heated greenhouse

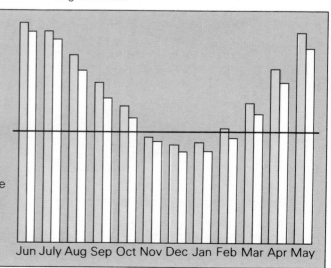

Quantity of radiation entering greenhouse

Jun July Aug Sep Oct Nov Dec Jan Feb Mar Apr May

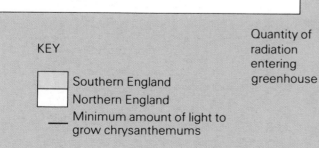

KEY

Southern England
Northern England
Minimum amount of light to grow chrysanthemums

2.4 *Storing and releasing energy*

Releasing the energy of plant sugars

Energy is needed by both plants and animals for life functions such as growth and movement. This energy is obtained by releasing the energy 'locked up' in sugars by a process called **respiration**. During respiration, **sugars** react with **oxygen** to make **carbon dioxide** and **water** and in doing so **energy** is released. All living things respire (but only plants can store the energy of sunlight by making sugars during photosynthesis).

Are the gases coming or going?

In plants, the processes of photosynthesis and respiration take place *at the same time* causing the carbon dioxide and oxygen each to flow in opposite directions. The plant's rate of respiration is always the same, as shown by the equal arrows on the diagram below, but the **rate of photosynthesis** depends on the amount of light.

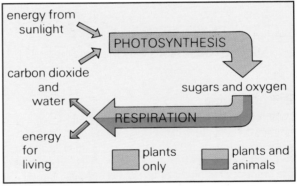

Notice the link between CO_2 needed by plants for photosynthesis and the CO_2 produced in respiration. The raw materials of photosynthesis are the end-products of respiration.

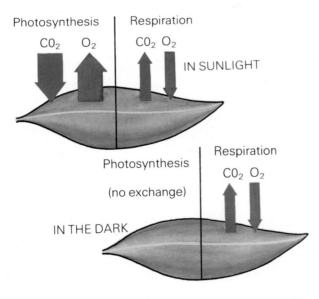

Exploring the rate of photosynthesis

Jacqui and June investigated the rate of photosynthesis over a full summer's day by punching discs of equal size from the leaves of a tree at different times and weighing them, after drying them.

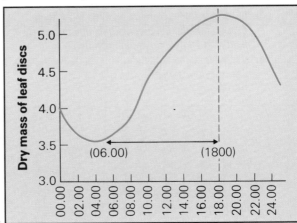

Why do you think the mass of the leaf increased between 06.00 to 18.00 hours?

Testing for carbon dioxide

Dawn and Ali decided to test the theory that plants provide the oxygen that animals need for respiration. Ali said that to make the test fair they would have to stop the animal getting any oxygen from the air. Dawn suggested that one way of stopping that was to do the test in a tube full of water. They chose pondweed as their plant, and water snails as their animals. They tested three different set-ups of pondweed and snails each in bright and dark conditions –and used an indicator to show the level of carbon dioxide in each tube.

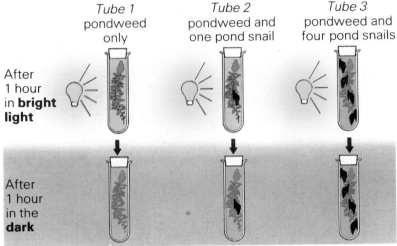

After 1 hour in **bright light**

After 1 hour in the **dark**

If the carbon dioxide level is low the indicator turns **blue**.

If the carbon dioxide level is high the indicator turns **green**.

Tube 1 pondweed only

Tube 2 pondweed and one pond snail

Tube 3 pondweed and four pond snails

After 1 hour in **bright light**

After 1 hour in the **dark**

> Which of these tubes shows that plants respire in the same way as animals?
>
> Which test(s) show(s) that plants produce more oxygen by photosynthesis than they use in respiration?

How do the plants get water for photosynthesis?

Plants use water as a raw material in photosynthesis – and yet they produce water by respiration. In bright conditions, plants produce ten times as much sugar during photosynthesis as they use in respiration. This uses up much of the water in their veins. Water also evaporates from the leaves by escaping from the stomata on the underside of the leaves. So, despite allowing the carbon dioxide needed for photosynthesis to enter the leaf, the stomata also allow water to escape. This loss of water through the leaves is called **transpiration**. The loss of water by transpiration is made good by the plant taking in more water through its roots from the soil.

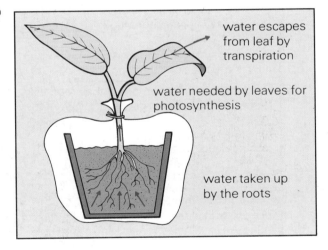

water escapes from leaf by transpiration

water needed by leaves for photosynthesis

water taken up by the roots

---

1 Why do living things need to respire? Draw arrows on a leaf to show the respiration and photosynthesis rates for a leaf in dim light.

2 Use the rate of photosynthesis graph to:
  a work out the approximate times of sunrise and sunset that day.
  b explain what is happening at 5.00 and 19.00.
  c explain why the final weight is greater after 24 hours.

3 In the pondweed/snail tests
  a what is needed from *outside* of the sealed tube to keep the community alive inside?
  b predict what will happen to the snails in *tube 3* if it is kept sealed.

4 A jar is filled with pondweed and water and the CO_2 indicator. When it is lowered 1 metre into a pond after an hour it shows blue. When the same thing is done at a depth of 3 metres, it shows neutral and at 6 metres deep, the indicator is green. Why?

2.5 *The flow of energy*

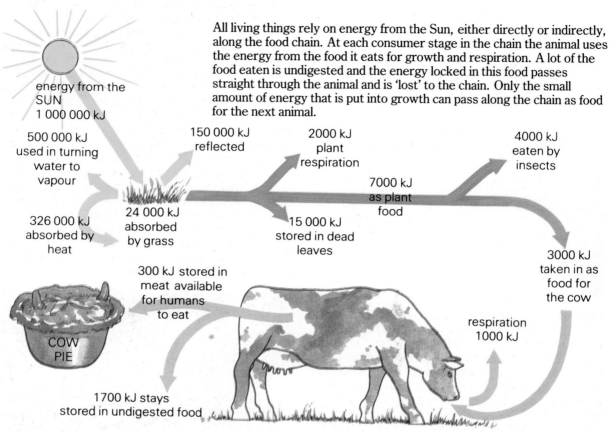

All living things rely on energy from the Sun, either directly or indirectly, along the food chain. At each consumer stage in the chain the animal uses the energy from the food it eats for growth and respiration. A lot of the food eaten is undigested and the energy locked in this food passes straight through the animal and is 'lost' to the chain. Only the small amount of energy that is put into growth can pass along the chain as food for the next animal.

energy from the
SUN
1 000 000 kJ

500 000 kJ
used in turning
water to
vapour

326 000 kJ
absorbed by
heat

24 000 kJ
absorbed
by grass

150 000 kJ
reflected

2000 kJ
plant
respiration

7000 kJ
as plant
food

15 000 kJ
stored in dead
leaves

4000 kJ
eaten by
insects

3000 kJ
taken in as
food for
the cow

respiration
1000 kJ

300 kJ stored in
meat available
for humans
to eat

COW
PIE

1700 kJ stays
stored in undigested food

1 What percentage of the food taken in by the cow is passed along the food chain?

2 Carnivores can digest more of their food than herbivores. If a person can digest 79% of the food eaten and 15% of the energy is used in respiration, how much energy of the food from the cow contributes to the person's growth?

Population problems

A balance exists in nature and certain factors control the numbers of each type of animal and plant. The amount of plant growth controls the number of herbivores, which in turn controls the number of carnivores. Disease and old age contribute to keeping numbers down, alongside hunger and predation. However, one animal has used its *intelligence* in such a way as to reduce the effects of these factors. Humans have developed weapons that can kill other animals, either for food or to prevent predation. We have also developed ways of *fighting disease* and *growing food more efficiently*, particularly in the last 200 years. As a result more humans are now being kept alive for a longer time and the population is growing at an ever increasing rate.

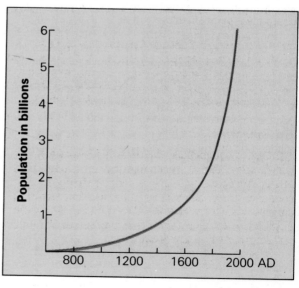

3 From the graph find the population in 1600, 1800 and 1900. From these figures can you estimate how long it will take the population of 4.0 billion in 1975 to become 8.0 billion?

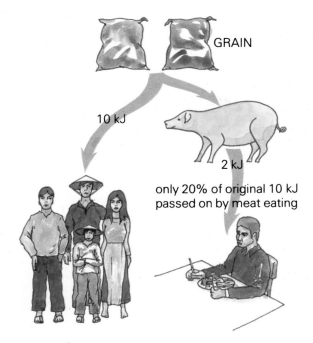

GRAIN

10 kJ

2 kJ

only 20% of original 10 kJ passed on by meat eating

Factory farming

Meat provides certain types of protein, which are not available from plants. In an attempt to produce meat as efficiently as possible, farmers consider the gain in the weight of the animal compared to the amount of food it eats. They do not want to continue feeding the animal once it stops growing. At first, most animals gain weight quite quickly as they grow. When they become adults this rate slows down or even stops. So from the farmer's point of view, it is more efficient to slaughter the animals when their growth rate begins to flatten out.

Some farmers use **factory farming** methods in which the animals are kept warm and their movement restricted so that their bodies do not use so much energy and they gain weight more quickly. Hormones are also used to increase meat and milk production.

Animal growth rates

Although most animals will follow a similar growth curve, some animals reach maturity far quicker than others and so the time axis is shorter. In poor countries it may be more useful to use fast maturing animals (such as chickens, fish or rabbits) as a source of protein since they produce an equivalent weight of meat sooner than, say, a cow.

| 4 | Pig food contains 13 500 kJ/kg and pork gives 22 000 kJ/kg. Assuming a human can eat all of the pig, calculate how much energy has been 'lost' in feeding a pig from 8 weeks to 24 weeks, which eats on average 10 kg of pig food per week. (8 wk weight 20 kg; final weight 90 kg). |

Feeding the people

There are 6 billion people in the world today but half a billion are undernourished – so one in every 12 people in the world does not get enough to eat. Of these 500 million underfed people, 40 million die from malnutrition every year. Imagine the world reaction to a disaster that killed *eight out of every ten* people in Britain. The equivalent of this happens *every year* in the world – this is the size of the problem. To feed the expanding population, more land is being used for farming every year. Rain forests are being cleared to make way for crops but this, along with pollution, can cause a change in the Earth's climate. Other areas are being overgrazed and overfarmed and the deserts are expanding, making the problem of supplying enough food even worse. At the same time that 1 in 12 people don't get enough to eat, people in America, Europe and Australia generally overeat. Meat is especially popular in these countries and *over a quarter* of the world's grain harvest is used for fattening animals for them. The 1 billion people in these countries eat $\frac{2}{3}$ of the world's total meat production.

Maize . . . or meat . . . what should we eat?

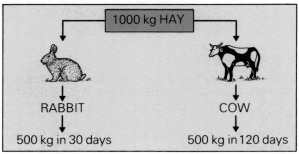

1000 kg HAY

RABBIT

500 kg in 30 days

COW

500 kg in 120 days

Rabbits and cows produce the same amount of meat from the hay – but rabbits do it faster!

| 5 | In a group, discuss the advantages and the disadvantages of factory farming animals when so many people die each year from hunger. |

2.6 *Natural cycles*

Why aren't things used up?

The materials that make up your body were part of something else before you came into being! These materials have been on Earth since it was formed and have been used in many forms over the years. The materials aren't used up because they are constantly being recycled. The chemicals involved join together, then break down, only to reform again – the pattern of life is forever changing. The many factors that control these cycles interact in a moving, or **dynamic**, way to maintain the balance.

The water cycle

The water cycle is one of nature's important processes. Water is essential to life and it is maintained in balance through the cyclical interaction of the environment. ▼

Below a certain temperature the invisible water vapour condenses into droplets that form clouds which can be seen.

water vapour rises by convection

if droplets get too heavy they fall as rain

energy from the sun

trees **transpire** and animals **respire** water vapour into the air

sea water evaporates into water vapour leaving the salt behind

without fresh water, land animals and plants would die

The carbon-oxygen cycle

Animals breathe in oxygen and breathe out carbon dioxide. Any animal trapped in an airtight place would soon die when all the available oxygen was used up. The Earth itself is like an airtight place surrounded by empty space – so what stops this happening on Earth . . .?

Air taken into the lungs contains:

nitrogen   78%
oxygen   21%
carbon dioxide 0.03%

Air breathed out of the lungs contains:

nitrogen   78%
oxygen   12%
carbon dioxide 9%

What does this information tell you about how air is changed inside the lungs?

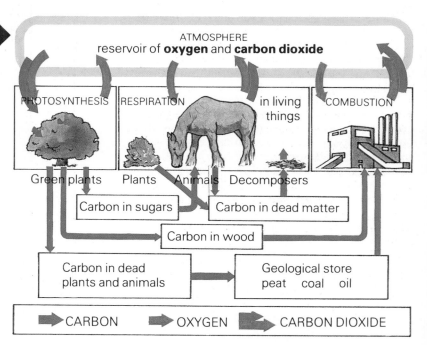

ATMOSPHERE
reservoir of **oxygen** and **carbon dioxide**

PHOTOSYNTHESIS   RESPIRATION   in living things   COMBUSTION

Green plants   Plants   Animals   Decomposers

Carbon in sugars   Carbon in dead matter

Carbon in wood

Carbon in dead plants and animals   Geological store
peat   coal   oil

➡ CARBON   ➡ OXYGEN   ➡ CARBON DIOXIDE

Maintaining the carbon/oxygen balance

By working in *opposite* directions, respiration and photosynthesis maintain a balanced atmosphere containing 20% oxygen but only 0.04% carbon dioxide. During **photosynthesis** plants give out ten times more oxygen than they take in during respiration. This surplus replaces all the oxygen used up during **combustion** (the burning of fuels) and animal **respiration**. By taking in carbon dioxide, the plants '*lock up*' carbon in the forms of starch and cellulose. Such carbon is not immediately available for recycling. Animals which eat the starch release the carbon as carbon dioxide during respiration. Any carbon 'locked up' in plants and animals when they die is recycled by the respiratory action of the **decomposers**. The more woody cellulose is slower to rot and may be compressed down into peat and finally into coal. Some carbon dioxide combines with calcium to form sea shells and these shells left on the sea bed can become compressed over time to form chalk.

Decaying forests no longer recycle gases into the air. Their carbon becomes locked up in coal and peat.

Early days

The water and the carbon-oxygen cycles have not always been in process. When the Earth was formed the atmosphere was made up of mainly **methane** and **ammonia** gases. The temperature was so great that any free oxygen reacted with these two gases to form **carbon dioxide**, **water vapour** and unreactive **nitrogen**. When the Earth cooled enough, water fell as rain, forming rivers and seas – this helped to cool the Earth even more quickly. The carbon dioxide was then used by the first plants to produce **food** by photosynthesis – which released **oxygen** into the air. Once the oxygen level was high enough, animal life began. For the last 200 million years, photosynthesis and respiration have maintained a *constant and necessary balance* between carbon dioxide and oxygen in the atmosphere – until now!

Upsetting the balance

In the last 200 years, millions of tonnes of coal and oil has been burnt for fuel. This has added much more carbon dioxide to the atmosphere. We humans are now upsetting the cycle by burning coal and oil faster than they are produced. Over the same period, vast numbers of trees in the rain forests have been cut down. These trees, through their photosynthesis, used to remove enormous quantities of carbon dioxide from the air and replace it with oxygen. But again people have interfered and upset the natural cycle on a large scale. As a result there is currently an increasing level of carbon dioxide in the atmosphere which may cause increased temperature due to the **greenhouse' effect** (*see 1.10*) – which may in turn affect the water cycle by altering the weather patterns.

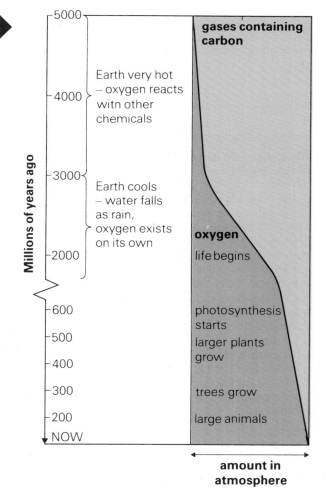

Millions of years ago

- 5000
- 4000 — Earth very hot – oxygen reacts with other chemicals
- 3000 — Earth cools – water falls as rain, oxygen exists on its own
- 2000 — **oxygen**, life begins
- 600 — photosynthesis starts
- 500 — larger plants grow
- 400
- 300 — trees grow
- 200 — large animals
- NOW

gases containing carbon

amount in atmosphere

---

1 Energy is needed to 'run' these natural cycles. What supplies this energy and what process does it start in
  a the water cycle
  b the carbon/oxygen cycle?

2 Why did the level of carbon dioxide in the air begin to fall
  a gradually, about 600 million years ago?
  b rapidly, about 250 million years ago?

2.7 *Nature and nitrogen*

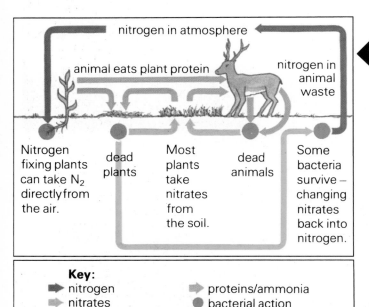

Key:
- ➡ nitrogen
- ➡ nitrates
- ➡ proteins/ammonia
- ● bacterial action

The diagram labels:
- nitrogen in atmosphere
- animal eats plant protein
- nitrogen in animal waste
- Nitrogen fixing plants can take N_2 directly from the air.
- dead plants
- Most plants take nitrates from the soil.
- dead animals
- Some bacteria survive – changing nitrates back into nitrogen.

The natural nitrogen cycle

All organisms grow by using 'building-blocks' called **amino acids** to produce **protein** for new cells. Animals can only gain many of their amino acid 'blocks' by eating plants or other animals, but plants produce *their own* amino acids using basic chemicals such as nitrogen. Although nitrogen makes up most of the atmosphere, most plants cannot make direct use of it. Instead they have to use **nitrate salts** from the soil as their source of nitrogen. Most of the nitrates taken from the soil in this way get back into the soil from animal faeces or from dead plants and animals. **Decomposers** cause the cells in the bodies to decay releasing nitrates from their proteins. Some plants have *bacteria* that live in swellings on their roots that can *'fix' nitrogen* directly from the air. Peas and beans are examples of such plants – they do not depend only on waste materials for their nitrates.

Large farms often spray fertiliser from the air onto the land.

Breaking the natural cycle

When plants are harvested, the nitrogen 'locked up' in the protein of the plants cannot be returned to the soil by decay. Other nutrients, such as **phosphates** and **potassium** are also lost in this way. If plants are repeatedly grown and harvested, untreated soil would lose all its goodness. The lost nutrients can be replaced by adding **organic** (natural) material such as manure or garden compost (decomposed plants). Large farms may not have enough animals to produce the manure and so they use **inorganic** or **artificial fertilisers** instead. Chemical factories can directly combine hydrogen and nitrogen to give ammonia. This ammonia is then mixed with phosphates and potassium to make a fertiliser called **NPK: N** for nitrogen (in ammonia NH_3), **P** for the phosphorus (in the phosphate) and **K** for potassium (chemical symbol **K**). In the last 20 years, the world use of fertilisers has increased four times from 20 kilotonnes to 80 kilotonnes.

The cost of fertilisers

The cost of adding fertilisers to soils is expensive but the increase in the amount of crops grown (yield) can be as much as ten times the cost of the fertiliser itself. To stay in business farmers need to make their farms produce more crops but be careful about spending too much money on fertiliser. When fertilisers are used, their effects are limited as the graph shows. Adding some fertiliser may make a big improvement, but adding still more will *not* increase the yield by anything like as much.

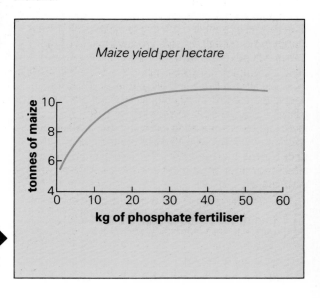

Maize yield per hectare

Graph: tonnes of maize (vertical axis, 4 to 10) against kg of phosphate fertiliser (horizontal axis, 0 to 60).

The other costs to the environment!

When artificial fertiliser is added to the land some of it will be dissolved by rain water and washed out of the soil. This process is called **leaching**. The dissolved fertilisers are eventually washed into the rivers and streams and can cause many problems . . . .

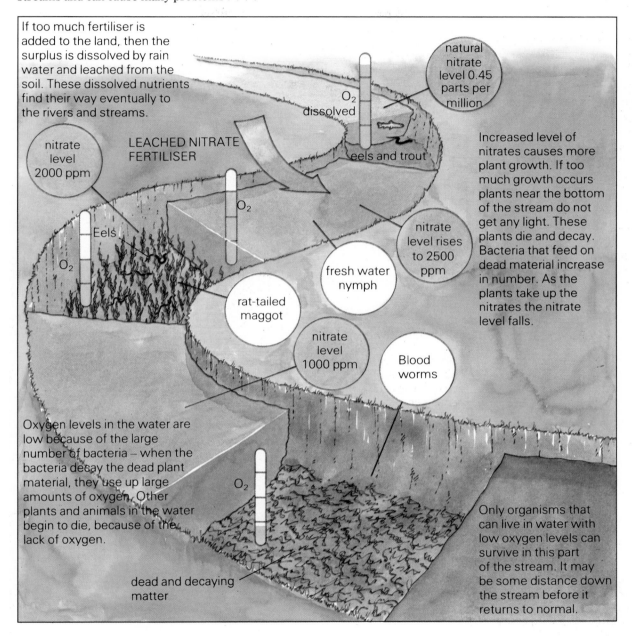

If too much fertiliser is added to the land, then the surplus is dissolved by rain water and leached from the soil. These dissolved nutrients find their way eventually to the rivers and streams.

nitrate level 2000 ppm

LEACHED NITRATE FERTILISER

Eels

O₂

natural nitrate level 0.45 parts per million

O₂ dissolved

eels and trout

O₂

fresh water nymph

nitrate level rises to 2500 ppm

rat-tailed maggot

nitrate level 1000 ppm

Blood worms

Increased level of nitrates causes more plant growth. If too much growth occurs plants near the bottom of the stream do not get any light. These plants die and decay. Bacteria that feed on dead material increase in number. As the plants take up the nitrates the nitrate level falls.

Oxygen levels in the water are low because of the large number of bacteria – when the bacteria decay the dead plant material, they use up large amounts of oxygen. Other plants and animals in the water begin to die, because of the lack of oxygen.

O₂

dead and decaying matter

Only organisms that can live in water with low oxygen levels can survive in this part of the stream. It may be some distance down the stream before it returns to normal.

1. Why do plants and animals need nitrogen?

2. The diagram of the nitrogen cycle does not include artificial fertilisers. Design and draw your *own* version of the nitrogen cycle *including* labelled arrows showing the use of such fertilisers.

3. A student wrote:– 'Because nitrogen does not react, the nitrogen in the air is of no use.' Do you agree? Explain your answer.

4. What are the effects of nitrates leaching from the soil on:
   a the nitrate levels in the river water?
   b the oxygen levels in the stream?
   c the animal life in the stream?

Waste-removal and recycling

Natural waste removal

Dead plant and animal material, or **detritus**, is broken down and digested by the 'decomposers'. The nutrients which are 'locked up' in the detritus are then returned to the soil. Materials that can be broken down (degraded) in this way are called **bio-degradable**. Similarly, animal faeces are decomposed by bacteria to form nitrates in the soil. The recycling of waste is a natural process but sometimes it can get out of hand . . .

Decomposer bacteria feed on the sewage and grow in large numbers using up dissolved oxygen.

As the sewage decomposes down river the bacteria drop in numbers and the stream slowly returns to normal.

Bacteria grow in large numbers where the sewage is most concentrated, taking oxygen from the algae which then die.

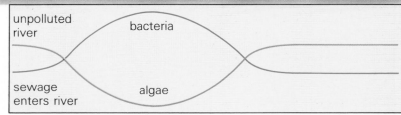

What a waste

Because so many people live in towns, the quantity of human waste is far too great for natural processes to deal with it. Together with other waste, such as washing-up water, this human waste forms what we call **sewage**. Each person in the UK produces about 200 litres of sewage every day. Sewage is 99% water but the remaining solid waste, dissolved chemicals and harmful micro-organisms must be treated. If untreated sewage is dumped directly into a river, the nitrogen-rich waste will feed a population explosion of decomposer bacteria. The bacteria will soon use up all the oxygen in the river, causing other life in the river to die.

Who needs oxygen?

Chemicals found in waste contain energy that is normally used by the decomposers during respiration. Once the decomposers have used up the oxygen, there may still be some waste left over. Different bacteria which do not need oxygen now take over the decompositon. These bacteria are called **methano-bacteria** because when digesting the waste they release the gas methane. Stagnant ponds and marshy bogs which contain large amounts of dead plant matter (but very little oxygen) are often the 'home' of methano-bacteria. The methane gas will rise to the top if the sludge is disturbed.

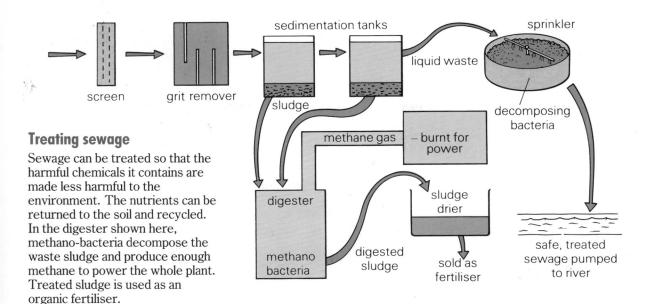

sedimentation tanks — sprinkler — liquid waste — decomposing bacteria

screen — grit remover — sludge

methane gas — – burnt for power

digester

methano bacteria — digested sludge

sludge drier — sold as fertiliser

safe, treated sewage pumped to river

Treating sewage

Sewage can be treated so that the harmful chemicals it contains are made less harmful to the environment. The nutrients can be returned to the soil and recycled. In the digester shown here, methano-bacteria decompose the waste sludge and produce enough methane to power the whole plant. Treated sludge is used as an organic fertiliser.

Making water safe to drink. ▶

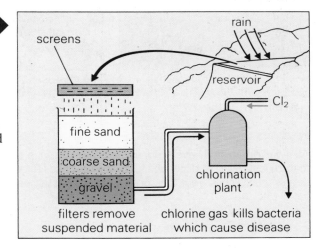

rain — screens — reservoir — Cl₂ — fine sand — coarse sand — gravel — chlorination plant

filters remove suspended material — chlorine gas kills bacteria which cause disease

Prevention better than cure

Apart from making sure that sewage is safe, it is important to make sure that the water we use is safe. Pure water is essential for healthy living. Much of the disease in the world is caused by contaminated water. Even in the UK, diseases such as typhoid, cholera and dysentry can be caught if our water becomes contaminated with sewage. The threat of disease can be defeated on a large scale by treating the water supply and on a small scale by washing hands after using the lavatory or before handling food.

Household waste

When household waste is disposed of in rubbish tips it is covered up by mountains of other rubbish. Methano-bacteria begin to decompose the rubbish producing methane gas deep within the tip. Sometimes houses are built on old tips which are still producing this explosive gas. Clearly this can pose a serious threat to those living in these houses!

▶

WASTE TIP GAS PUTS THOUSANDS AT RISK!

Highly explosive methane gas from waste tips is threatening thousands of homes. A report calls for at least 600 tips to be fitted with equipment to control the escaping gas. People are often living within 100 m of these tips. Each year 18 million tonnes of domestic rubbish is put into holes in the ground in this country.

1 Why do the leaves that fall from trees disappear?

2 Draw a graph of the oxygen content of the river of which the algae/bacteria contents are shown on the opposite page.

3 Explain, in simple terms, why a natural fertiliser, like untreated sewage, can kill the wildlife in a river.

4 Why is methane gas not produced by normal decomposition?

3.1 Maintaining life

What is a living organism?

What features distinguish living organisms from non-living things? You can find the answer to this question by examining what living organisms *do,* and the *processes* that take place inside them. Look at these photographs. How can you tell which are living organisms and which are not?

This crystal grows by using the materials that surround it. Is it living?

What does this marmot have in common with the flower it is eating? In what ways do they differ?

Are these pebbles or beans? How can you tell which could be living material?

Features of living organisms

All living organisms have *seven* important features in common. Each feature is needed to maintain life. Some of these features are easier to detect than others – but they are *all* characteristics of living organisms.

What changes take place when something dies?

All living organisms release energy by **respiration**.

All living organisms **excrete**.

All living organisms **move**.

All living organisms **respond to changes in their surroundings** . . . the sight of food!

All living organisms **feed**.

All living organisms **reproduce** . . . and **grow**.

Clear signs of life

You can usually see an animal move – **movement** is one of the clearest signs of life. As well as being able to move from place to place, there are also movements taking place inside your body, such as your heart beat, your lungs expanding and contracting – clear signs that you are alive! Movements in plants are less obvious. Their movements are so slow that you cannot see them happening.

Movements often take place as a result of changes in the surroundings of a living organism – like running away from a predator. By **responding to change**, an organism *increases* its chance of survival.

Making new life

Living organisms do not live for ever. Each type of organism continues to *maintain* the life of its **species** by producing offspring through **reproduction**. Only *living* organisms can reproduce. Most organisms start life as a single cell which then divides many times during growth to produce thousands of cells. As new cells are formed, they become *specialised* to carry out different jobs. So organisms become more complex as they grow and increase in size and mass. ▼

Some flowers open and close depending on the amount of light. The opening and closing is too slow for your eye to detect.

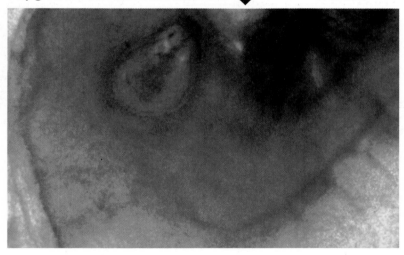

Like all organisms, you began your life as a single cell which grew to form a complex living organism. This picture shows a human embryo after 4 weeks growth. Its cells are becoming more specialised – the oval outline (to the left) will form the head, and the faint red line (curving from left up to the right) will form the spine.

Life from chemical reactions

All living organisms need a supply of **food** to stay alive. Animals take in ready-made food. Green plants make their own food using energy from sunlight. Food substances are then changed by chemical reactions which take place inside cells. Food is changed to produce substances needed to make new cells for **growth**, and to release energy during **respiration**. Chemical reactions in cells also form waste products which are removed by the process of **excretion**.

These seven features of living organisms – movement; response to changes; growth; feeding; respiration; excretion; reproduction – are all essential for the *maintenance of life*. You can read more about living organisms and their functions throughout this chapter.

1 | Which features does a robot have in common with a human? How does it differ?

2 | Which of the seven features are you doing all the time?

3.2 Healthy eating

What are you eating?

Do you have any idea of what is in the food you eat? What effect do different foods have on your body? You have to eat a balance of different food to stay healthy. You need to know *what* you should eat and *why* you should eat it so that you will choose a healthy combination of foods.

These shapes contain information about some common foods. Link the food product to the right shape to find out what each food contains.

NUTRITIONAL INFORMATION (Average values per 100 g of food)

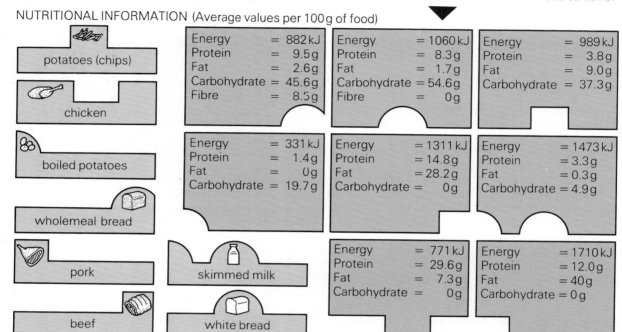

potatoes (chips)

chicken

boiled potatoes

wholemeal bread

pork

skimmed milk

beef

white bread

Energy = 882 kJ	
Protein = 9.5 g	
Fat = 2.6 g	
Carbohydrate = 45.6 g	
Fibre = 8.5 g	

Energy = 1060 kJ
Protein = 8.3 g
Fat = 1.7 g
Carbohydrate = 54.6 g
Fibre = 0 g

Energy = 989 kJ
Protein = 3.8 g
Fat = 9.0 g
Carbohydrate = 37.3 g

Energy = 331 kJ
Protein = 1.4 g
Fat = 0 g
Carbohydrate = 19.7 g

Energy = 1311 kJ
Protein = 14.8 g
Fat = 28.2 g
Carbohydrate = 0 g

Energy = 1473 kJ
Protein = 3.3 g
Fat = 0.3 g
Carbohydrate = 4.9 g

Energy = 771 kJ
Protein = 29.6 g
Fat = 7.3 g
Carbohydrate = 0 g

Energy = 1710 kJ
Protein = 12.0 g
Fat = 40 g
Carbohydrate = 0 g

A healthy diet

You need many different substances (**nutrients**) from food to remain healthy. A healthy diet contains **carbohydrates, fats, proteins, minerals, vitamins** and **fibre** in the correct amounts. These nutrients provide you with energy you need to live and raw materials to grow and replace worn out cells.

The body's fuel

Carbohydrates are your body's main fuel. They are to your body what petrol is to a car. The energy that carbohydrates contain is released during **respiration** and used up as your body functions e.g. when you move, breathe, when your heart beats.

There are three kinds of carbohydrate – **sugars, starch** and **cellulose.** Jam and sweet fruits are examples of sugary foods. Bread and potatoes are examples of starchy foods. Cellulose is present in plant foods, such as cereals, fruit and vegetables. It is the fibre in your diet.

Starch is made from long chains of **glucose** molecules. Glucose is a simple sugar and there may be several hundred in each starch molecule.

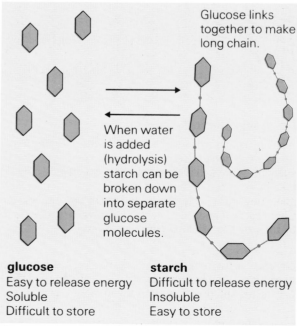

Glucose links together to make long chain.

When water is added (hydrolysis) starch can be broken down into separate glucose molecules.

glucose
Easy to release energy
Soluble
Difficult to store

starch
Difficult to release energy
Insoluble
Easy to store

Starch is made from the same repeated unit (glucose).

42

Stores of energy

Fats (and oils) are found in milk, meat, and in vegetable oils such as sunflower oil. The table opposite shows that fats contain much more energy than carbohydrates and proteins, so they are useful stores of energy. Fat helps to insulate the body against heat loss so it is stored beneath the skin. It can also act as a protective cushion so it is stored around the heart and kidneys.

Nutrient	Energy content in 1 g
carbohydrate	17 kJ
fat	38 kJ
protein	17 kJ

A comparison of the energy content in nutrients.

The body's building material

Proteins provide the raw materials your body needs to build new cells and to repair damaged cells. Your body is made from thousands of different types of protein. A single protein molecule may contain hundreds or thousands of smaller units called **amino acids.** There are twenty different amino acids which are linked to chains to form proteins. Any amino acid can be repeated many times along the chain.

Humans can make half of the 20 natural amino acids. The ten that you cannot make have to obtained from your diet. These are the **essential amino acids.**

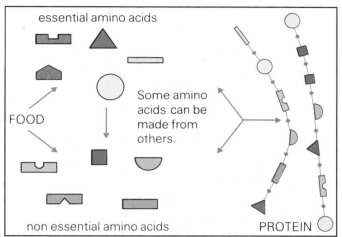

Different proteins are made by arranging amino acids in different orders. This means that many types of protein can be made to perform many different jobs.

A balancing act

Your diet needs to provide sufficient energy and the various substances required for growth and repair. You also need sufficient minerals and vitamins. To stay healthy you need to *balance* what you eat with what you need. In other words you need to have a **balanced diet.**

*A person who has a poor diet suffers from **malnutrition** (**mal** = bad). Malnutrition is a term for any type of long term dietry imbalance, not to be confused with starvation (marasmus).*

Nutrient g/100 g	Eggs	Cheddar cheese	Pork sausages	Fruit cake
carbohydrate	0	0	0	55.0
protein	11.9	25.4	12.0	4.6
fat	12.3	34.5	40.0	15.9

It is difficult to choose the right diet unless you know the content of the foods you buy. This table shows the nutrient ingredients of some common foods.

1   **a** What important groups of nutrients are *not* listed in the table?
     b Which contains the most energy 100 g of cheddar cheese or 100 g of pork sausages?

3.3 Food and energy

Energy to work, rest and play

Most of the food you eat each day is used to provide your body with energy. What is this energy used for?

The amount of energy that you use over a period of time is called your **metabolic** rate. Even when you are resting you use energy to breathe, to pump blood around your body, and you use it to keep warm. The amount of energy you use at rest is your **basic energy requirement.** You use this basic amount of energy *plus* extra energy to carry out activities such as school work, walking or running around.

The daily energy requirements of different people. ▼

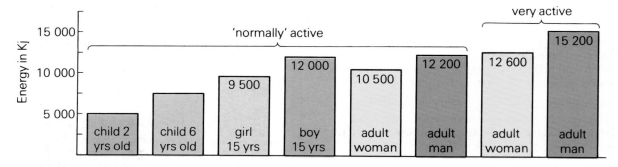

How much energy do you need?

The total amount of energy you need each day depends on how active you are, how old you are and whether you are male or female. It is not easy to separate these factors – some men do very physically demanding jobs, this may well distort upwards the average figure for energy used by men. The average daily energy needs of an adult man is currently 12 000 kJ and 9000 kJ for an adult female. Children require more energy in proportion to their body mass than adults. Energy needs per kg of body mass are highest in newborn babies and this decreases with age.

If a women and a man, both of the same weight and equal age, did the same job and the same amount of work at home, would their energy requirements be equal?

Age (years)	(male) Daily energy requirement (kJ)	(male) Average mass (kg)
0–1	3500	7
4–6	7600	20
10–12	10800	36
13–15	12000	50
17–19	13000	65
Adult	12000	70

The average daily energy requirements of males at various ages.

A balanced diet of foods like this will provide the average person with enough energy without causing a build up of fat.

Getting the balance right

In a balanced diet the energy you use comes mainly from carbohydrate. If you do not eat enough of this type of food, proteins and fats in the diet are used to provide the energy. When people take in less energy than they need, their body has to use the energy in stored food, particularly stored fat. This causes them to lose weight. If you want to slim sensibly it is necessary to maintain a balanced diet while eating fewer kilojoules than are used up.

Food that is eaten in excess of the body's needs is stored mainly as fat causing people to put on weight. Even carbohydrates and protein can be changed to fat and stored.

The amount of energy in food

Different foods produce different amounts of energy depending on the amount of protein, carbohydrate and fat that they contain. It is possible to measure the amount of energy in a food by burning the food in a **calorimeter**.

Calculating the energy in food

A given amount of any substance always requires the same amount of energy to produce a particular increase in temperature. For example,

1 g of water needs ....**4.2 J** to make its temperature rise by 1°C

so 250 g of water needs   250   ×   **4.2 J** to make its temperature rise by 1°C

For a bigger increase in temperature (e.g. 10°C);

Energy needed to raise
temperature of 250 g of
water by 10°C   = 250   ×   **4.2J** × 10
                     = 10 500 J
                     = 10.5 kJ

Using the calorimeters shown above, the amount of energy produced by burning of food can be calculated as follows:

Energy produced by
burning 1 g of food   = mass of   × **4.2 J** × the rise in temperature (°C)
                            water (g)

Example: Mass of water = 250 g, starting temperature = 18°C, final temperature = 27°C

Energy produced by
burning 1 g food   = 250   ×   **4.2 J** × (27 − 18)
                     = 9450 J

On food packets, food energy values are often given as 'energy per 100 g' because 100 g represents roughly the amount that someone is likely to eat in one portion.

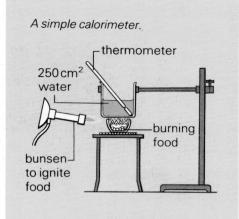

A simple calorimeter.

thermometer

250 cm² water

burning food

bunsen to ignite food

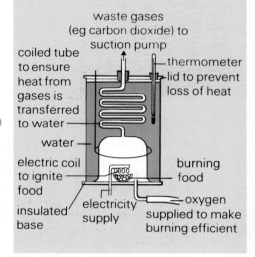

An advanced calorimeter.

waste gases (eg carbon dioxide) to suction pump

coiled tube to ensure heat from gases is transferred to water

thermometer

lid to prevent loss of heat

water

electric coil to ignite food

burning food

insulated base

electricity supply

oxygen supplied to make burning efficient

▲ The design of the calorimeter will affect the accuracy of the measurement of energy in the foods under investigation.

1. Why do children use up more energy per kg of body mass than adults?

2. When the amount of energy in 1 g of breakfast cereal was measured using a simple calorimeter the temperature of the water increased by 6°C. When the same amount of cereal was burned in the advanced calorimeter the temperature increase was 10°C. Give *three* reasons why the design of the advanced calorimeter produces a higher reading.

3. When 1 g of peanuts were burned in a calorimeter containing 250 g of water it gave a temperature rise of 11°C. 1 g of peas burned in the same calorimeter gave a temperature rise of 7°C. Calculate the energy content of both foods.

4. Leanne is on a slimming diet. Her total daily intake is 9000 kJ. Her basic energy requirement is 240 kJ per hour. In an average day she spends 8 hours sleeping, 7 hours at work in an office, mostly sitting at a desk using an additional 150 kJ per hour and 5 hours in various activities using an additonal 260 kJ per hour. She also spends 4 hours watching TV using an additional 60 kJ per hour. Will Leanne lose or gain weight. Explain your answer

3.4 *Too much or too little*

Malnutrition or bad nutrition can be caused by eating too little of the right foods or too much of the wrong foods!

The hungry and the greedy

You need to eat the right amounts of food to remain fit and healthy. Eating too little, too much or eating the wrong kinds of food can result in malnutrition – bad nutrition. Different races have their own characteristic diets. The East African Masai diet of berries, grain, vegetables, meat, and the milk and blood of cattle is as nutritious as a balanced British diet. However, in many developing countries malnutrition is a constant problem because a balanced diet is not available. Each year 40 million people, many children, die from hunger or hunger-related diseases. Malnutrition also occurs in well developed countries such as the UK but the main reason in such cases is *overeating* as opposed to food shortage! Over 40% of adults in the UK are overweight and are likely to suffer health problems as a result.

Eating too little

The average daily energy intake in many developing countries falls below the minimum needed to stay healthy and maintain body weight. The body uses up stores of energy such as fat when the diet fails to provide sufficient energy. During prolonged starvation the body's own flesh is used up to supply the energy needed to stay alive. The body then wastes away and lacks the energy to move or fight off disease.

A diet which may contain sufficient energy content from fats and carbohydrates but lacks proteins will lead to illness and eventually death. In many countries illness due to protein deficiency is common. Kwashiorkor is a severe disease caused by a deficiency of protein. It is common in young children and babies who are fed on a starchy, protein-deficient diet.

Proteins which contain the essential amino acids are called first class proteins. Most animal proteins are in this category. Plant proteins often lack one or more of the essential amino acids so it is necessary to eat a wide variety of plant foods to obtain all the amino acids that the body needs. In many parts of Africa and Asia protein deficiency diseases are common because a varied diet of plant foods or a diet containing animal protein is unobtainable. An adult needs about 60 to 80 grammes of protein each day.

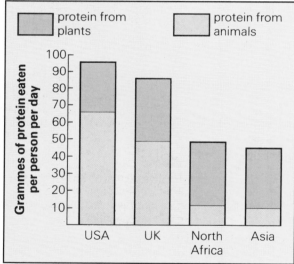

The average daily total of protein eaten by people in different parts of the world.

Comparing diets

The pie charts show the diets of two 12-year-old girls, one living in a town in England, and the other in a village in Mali – a drought prone African country.

■ Which of the two girls do you think has a healthier diet?

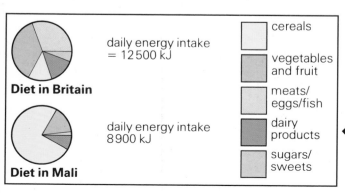

daily energy intake = 12 500 kJ

Diet in Britain

daily energy intake 8900 kJ

Diet in Mali

cereals

vegetables and fruit

meats/ eggs/fish

dairy products

sugars/ sweets

Eating too much

You can see from the table opposite that many adults living in the UK are overweight. If you eat more food than your body needs you are likely to store the surplus as fat and so become overweight. You are taking in more energy in the form of food, than you are using up. Becoming excessively overweight is called **obesity**. Obese people are more likely to suffer health problems such as heart disease and high blood pressure than those of normal weight.

Age group (years)	% overweight	
	Men	**Women**
20–29	25	21
30–39	40	25
40–49	52	38
50–59	49	47

Why do you think there is a greater percentage of overweight men in all the age groups shown in the table?

Too much fat

Excess fat in the diet is a main cause of obesity. About 42% of the average UK daily energy intake comes from fat. Eating too much fat can lead to a fatty layer developing on the inside wall of arteries. This layer, called an atheroma, builds up over a number of years narrowing the artery so that blood flow slows down or even stops. Such blockages are very dangerous especially when they occur in the blood flow to the heart or brain. The fatty layer contains a substance called **cholesterol.** Many health experts believe that by eating too much fat, particularly animal fat, you raise the cholesterol level in the blood and increase the risk of heart disease. Foods containing polyunsaturated fats, such as margarine and oil from sunflower seeds, may reduce the amount of cholesterol in the body.

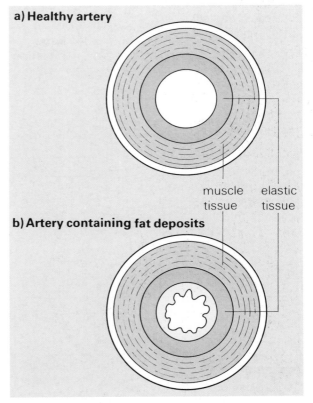

a) **Healthy artery**

muscle tissue   elastic tissue

b) **Artery containing fat deposits**

*Cross sectional diagrams of the artery of **a)** a healthy person and **b)** someone who is grossly overweight.*

Too little fibre

The typical diet in developed countries such as the UK contains a high proportion of sugars and fats but a low **fibre** content. Fibre is a carbohydrate which is not broken down or absorbed by the body. A shortage of fibre can lead to diseases of the gut such as bowel cancer and appendicitis. These are typically "western" diseases and are seldom found in developing countries where the diet contains a higher proportion of fibre.

1
  a Explain how the diet of the girl living in Mali will affect her health.
  b Give two reasons why the English girl's diet is unbalanced. How will this diet affect her health?

2
  a Which age group in the UK has the largest percentage of overweight people?
  b Which age group has the largest difference between men and women who are overweight?
  c What substance in the body forms the extra weight? How does this substance lead to health problems?

3 Use the histogram showing the amounts of protein eaten in different countries to answer the following questions
  a In which country is most protein eaten?
  b Which countries eat more plant protein than animal protein?
  c Give two reasons why many Asians suffer from diseases caused by a deficiency of protein?

4 Why are bowel cancer and heart disease called "western diseases"?

3.5 Cutting your food down to size

The human gut showing its main regions. ▼

mouth. Here food is broken down into smaller pieces. You can't swallow an apple whole! . . . .

. . . **gullet (oesophagus).** This carries food from the mouth to the stomach. . .

. . . **stomach.** Here food can be stored up to six hours . . .

. . . **small intestine.** This is a very long coiled part of the gut. If it is uncoiled the whole gut measures 10 metres (adult). This is where food gets into the body . . .

large intestine

waste

. . . **anus.** Waste leaves the body from here.

food

waste

molecules enter bloodstream through gut wall

What happens to food after you have chewed it and swallowed it? When it leaves your mouth it goes to your stomach and to other parts of your **alimentary canal** or **gut.** You can see from the diagram opposite that the gut is a very long tube running through your body. Food is pushed along the gut by a wave-like action called **peristalsis.** This action pushes food along in a similar way to squeezing the last bit of toothpaste out if its tube!

What happens inside your gut?

Before you can make use of food as energy it has to pass through the wall of the gut and enter the bloodstream. You can find out how food molecules pass through the gut wall by making a model of the gut. The model is made from visking tubing which is similar to the gut wall in the way that it allows some molecules to pass through it. A mixture of starch and glucose solution are placed inside the tubing which is then placed into a boiling tube of water. Starch molecules are made up of long chains of glucose units. The water surrounding the tubing is tested at intervals for starch (iodine test) and glucose (Benedict's test).

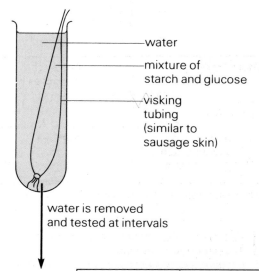

water

mixture of starch and glucose

visking tubing (similar to sausage skin)

water is removed and tested at intervals

	2 min	20 min
Iodine	solution stays deep red	solution stays deep red
Benedict's test	solution stays blue	solution becomes brick red

Through the use of a model made of visking tubing you can see what happens to food in the human gut.

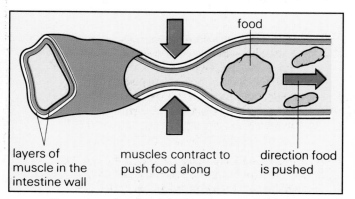

food

layers of muscle in the intestine wall

muscles contract to push food along

direction food is pushed

*The action of **peristalsis**, pushing your food along the gut.*

Making big molecules smaller

The gut model investigation shows that only small molecules (e.g. glucose) can pass through the gut wall and enter the bloodstream. Much of your food is in the form of long molecules (e.g. starch) which have to be broken down so they can be used by the body. As food passes along your gut various juices are added to it. Saliva is mixed with food while it is in your mouth. More juices are added from the stomach, then from the liver and the pancreas, and finally from the small intestine. The gut juices and saliva contain special chemicals called **enzymes** that break down large food molecules into smaller ones by a process called **digestion.**

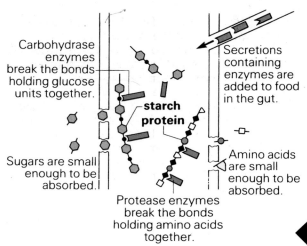

Carbohydrase enzymes break the bonds holding glucose units together.

Secretions containing enzymes are added to food in the gut.

starch
protein

Sugars are small enough to be absorbed.

Amino acids are small enough to be absorbed.

Protease enzymes break the bonds holding amino acids together.

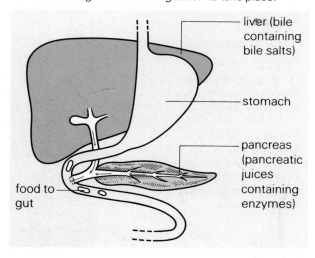

Liquids from the liver and the pancreas are added to food in the gut to enable digestion to take place. ▼

liver (bile containing bile salts)

stomach

pancreas (pancreatic juices containing enzymes)

food to gut

The right tools for the job

Each kind of food molecule requires a specific kind of enzyme to break it down just as a certain key will only open one type of lock. Protein-splitting enzymes will only break down proteins – they have no effect on starch or fats. You can see from the diagrams that the enzymes break down food molecules into separate units. Long chain food molecules become digested into their separate units.

◄ *Enzymes in the gut break down food into smaller molecules.*

Where from	Name of enzyme	What the enzyme works on (substrate)	Products of digestion
stomach small intestine	protease	protein	amino acids
saliva, pancreas small intestine	carbohydrase	starch and other carbohydrates	glucose
pancreas	lipase	fats	fatty acids, glycerol

The table summarises the main digestive enzymes at work in the human gut.

1 Use the results of the model gut investigation to answer the following:
  a What food substance, if any, is present in the water after i) 2 mins?
        ii) 20 mins?
  b Which of the two substances used cannot pass through the gut wall?
  c What can this substance be changed into so that the body can use it?

2 **a** In the same experiment what part of the body is represented by i) the visking tubing and ii) the distilled water?
  b How would you explain the results of this experiment if starch *and* glucose were present in the distilled water after two minutes?

3 Cellulose is a long chain carbohydrate found in vegetable and fruit. You do not produce an enzyme that can digest cellulose so what do you think will happen to the cellulose in your diet?

3.6 *Getting food into the body*

What happens to digested food?

Once foods have been broken down to form small soluble molecules the process of digestion is complete. Molecules of digested food are small enough to be absorbed through the gut wall. They are also soluble so that they will dissolve in the bloodstream which transports them to all parts of the body.

tiny blood vessels (capillaries)

muscular wall of intestine

What features can you see in this photograph that make the gut wall very efficient at absorbing food?

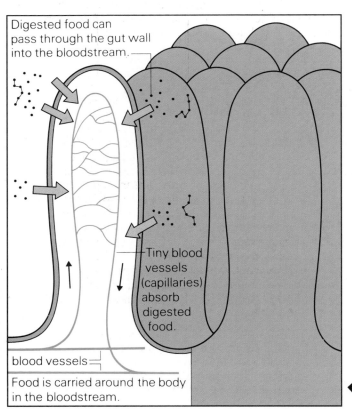

Digested food can pass through the gut wall into the bloodstream.

Tiny blood vessels (capillaries) absorb digested food.

blood vessels

Food is carried around the body in the bloodstream.

Getting food into the body

The small intestine is very efficient at taking in digested food because its structure is ideally suited to the job of absorbing food:
- it is long so that there is a large area for absorbing food,
- its inner surface contains thousands of tiny folds called **villi** which produce a huge surface area for the food to pass through,
- each villus contains many tiny blood vessels (capillaries) to carry away absorbed food,
- each villus is very thin so that absorbed food can easily reach the bloodstream.

Transporting food

The small molecules of digested food pass through the cells lining each villus, then through the walls of capillaries and into the bloodstream. Here the food molecules dissolve in blood **plasma** – the liquid part of blood. Blood is transported to all parts of the body along a network of blood **vessels.**

◀ *Each villus contains many tiny blood vessels to carry away absorbed food.*

Providing the body with energy

All cells in the body need glucose for their supplies of energy to stay alive. Glucose passes from the blood into cells where it is combined with oxygen to release energy during respiration. (You can find out more about respiration on spread 3.7).

Immediately after a meal the amount of glucose in the blood rises as it is produced during digestion and gets absorbed into the body from the small intestine. Too much blood glucose is harmful so the excess is stored in the forms of glycogen and fat until it is needed. Glycogen is made by joining many glucose molecules together to form a long chain molecule (similar to starch) – it is then stored in the liver. Fat is stored under the skin and around the major organs of the body. ▶

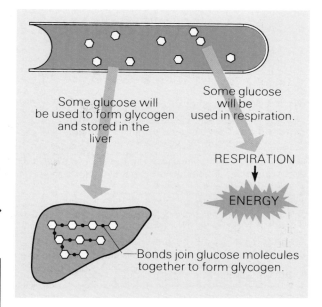

Some glucose will be used to form glycogen and stored in the liver

Some glucose will be used in respiration.

RESPIRATION

ENERGY

Bonds join glucose molecules together to form glycogen.

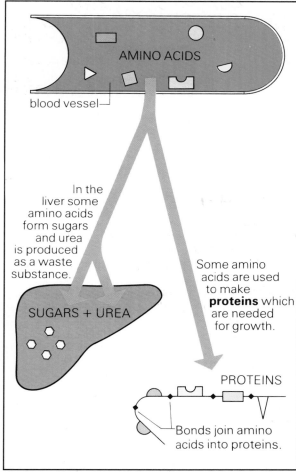

AMINO ACIDS

blood vessel

In the liver some amino acids form sugars and urea is produced as a waste substance.

SUGARS + UREA

Some amino acids are used to make **proteins** which are needed for growth.

PROTEINS

Bonds join amino acids into proteins.

Amino acids are taken in through your diet, or made by your body (see 3.2) to form proteins and stores of glycogen.

Providing the body with building material

Amino acids are used to make proteins – the building material of the body. Each protein is a long chain molecule formed from hundreds of amino acid molecules. Amino acids which are not needed to make proteins are used to make stores of glycogen and fat. When this happens the nitrogen-containing part of the amino acid is removed. This forms a waste substance called **urea** which is removed from the body in the kidneys. This waste has been produced by reactions in the body's cells i.e. it was not present in this form in the original food. Removal of this waste is called **excretion** (*see 3.13*).

Getting rid of waste

After digestion and absorption, the small intestine contains some food that the body cannot digest. The enzymes produced in the human gut cannot break down cellulose and plant fibres (roughage) and these pass along the small intestine without being broken down. The roughage passes into the large intestine where it stays for about 36 hours. Water is essential for life and so during this time most of the water that is in the large intestine is reabsorbed to prevent the body from dehydrating. This leaves behind semi-solid waste called **faeces.** The waste is expelled from the body through the anus. This waste has not left the gut since eating. It was present in the food before eating and so it is *not* formed by the body. The removal of this waste is called **defaecation** (egestion).

1   **a** What substances are absorbed into the body from the small intestine?
    b What do all these substances have in common?

2   What features of the small intestine make it very good for absorbing food?

3   List the ways that the body can store an excess of carbohydrate that is taken in with the diet.

3.7 Releasing energy

Sources of energy

Many substances such as coal, oil, natural gas, sugar, and fat have energy stored in them. The most common way to release this energy is to combine the substance with oxygen. When fuels such as coal are oxidised their energy is released quickly. When foods are oxidised in your body their energy is released slowly.

Quick energy release

When coal and other fuels are heated they start to burn and the energy released very quickly can be used to heat homes, cook food and provide power for car and motorbike engines. This quick release of energy occurs during **combustion**. During this process, oxygen in the air combines with the fuel to form oxides. For example, coal contains carbon which burns to form carbon dioxide. You can read more about this in the Energy chapter in the Physics book (Chapter 2).

Slow energy release

Foods also store energy – they are your body's fuel. You need energy for growth, keeping warm and for activities such as cycling. The energy that you use comes from the energy in food. Glucose is the main food that the cells of your body use to release energy. The energy stored in glucose is released by the process of **respiration.** During respiration glucose combines with oxygen to release energy. Carbon dioxide and water are also produced as by-products.

glucose + oxygen → carbon dioxide + water + energy

The energy contained in glucose is released in stages rather than all at once. This makes respiration different from combustion. The diagram opposite shows how glucose is broken down by a series of reactions during respiration. This slow release of energy during respiration is only possible because enzymes are present in cells first to *get* the reactions going and then *keep* them going.

In the presence of oxygen from the air glucose can be *completely* broken down. This process is called **aerobic respiration.**

Fuels in the motorbike engine release energy quickly. Energy from the bicyclist's food is released more slowly — sometimes this feels like hard work!

Several enzymes are needed to break down glucose to make it react with oxygen. Energy is then released at each reaction. ▼

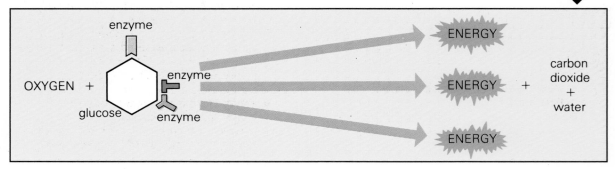

Respiration without oxygen

Sometimes your body cannot get enough oxygen. For example, during strenuous activity, such as fast sprinting, the supply of oxygen to your muscles can become insufficient. This also happens in 'explosive' athletics events such as in the shot put. The muscles of the athlete in the photograph will be using up all the oxygen available to release energy from glucose but will still need more energy. To provide the energy that is needed, some glucose breaks down without using oxygen. This process is called **anaerobic respiration.** In this process lactic acid is produced instead of carbon dioxide and water.

glucose → lactic acid + energy

Anaerobic respiration can only take place for a short time because the build up of lactic acid stops muscles from working by causing fatigue.

◀ *A sudden release of energy is needed during 'explosive' athletic activity. This is released without needing oxygen, during anaerobic respiration.*

Inefficient use of glucose

The amount of energy released during anaerobic respiration is much less than from aerobic respiration. Aerobic respiration releases almost twenty times more energy than anaerobic respiration. This is because glucose has been incompletely broken down during anaerobic respiration and some energy is still stored in lactic acid.

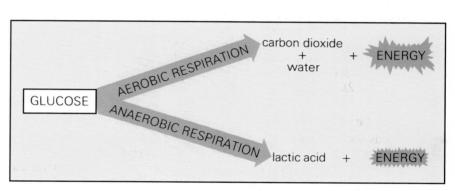

How much oxygen do you need?

Respiration takes place in all living cells. Oxygen needed for respiration is taken into your body as you breathe. The amount of oxygen that cells use depends on how much energy is needed. The table shows the amount of oxygen breathed in and the energy that is needed during various activities.

Activity	Amount of oxygen breathed in (litres per min)	Energy needed (kJ per min)
lying down	0.20	4
sitting	0.30	6
walking	1.50	30
jogging	4.00	80

1. The table shows that a person sleeping uses 4 kJ of energy per minute. What is this energy used for?

2. Why does the amount of oxygen breathed in increase as physical activity becomes more strenuous?

3. Walking uses 30 kJ of energy per minute. Inhaled air contains 20% oxygen. How much air must be breathed in each minute during walking?

4. Olympic athletes use up 200 kJ of energy during a 100 metre race.
   a. Use the information in the table to predict how much oxygen athletes will breathe during a 100 metre race.
   b. When the amount of oxygen the athletes breathed was measured it was found to be less than 0.5 litres. Explain why this measured value is different from your prediction.
   c. An athlete uses up about 14 000 kJ of energy running a marathon. The total amount of oxygen they breathe in is 700 litres. Do marathon runners obtain energy from aerobic or anaerobic respiration?

3.8 Exchanging gases

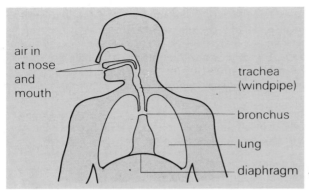

air in at nose and mouth

trachea (windpipe)

bronchus

lung

diaphragm

What happens when you breathe in?

When you breathe in, gases from the air, containing mainly oxygen and nitrogen, enter at the nose and mouth. Air is forced into and out of the lungs by the action of the diaphragm and the rib cage. They then pass along a passageway called the **trachea.** This branches out at its end into two short tubes called **bronchi.** These tubes lead to every part of the lungs through numerous branches called **bronchioles.**

◀ *Air passes along the trachea into the lungs where gases enter and leave the body.*

▼ *Diffusion can take place in a gas, such as when perfume spreads out into the air . . .*

. . . or in a liquid such as when coffee particles spread out in water in a cup of instant coffee. ▲

What happens in the lungs?

In the lungs, the oxygen needed for respiration goes into the blood. The carbon dioxide produced by respiration leaves the blood. This is called **gaseous exchange** and takes place by a process called **diffusion.** Diffusion is the movement of particles from a region where they are in high concentration to another region where they are in low concentration.

What are the lungs made of?

The lungs are designed to make the process of gaseous exchange very efficient. Each bronchiole leads to a bunch of tiny balloons or air sacs called **alveoli.** This gives the lungs a much greater surface area over which diffusion can occur than if they were made of one large balloon or air sac.

Each small balloon has a volume of 200 cm³ and a surface area of 150 cm³.

volume = 1000 cm³ surface area = 600 cm²

Five balloons can have the same volume, but a larger surface area, than one large balloon.

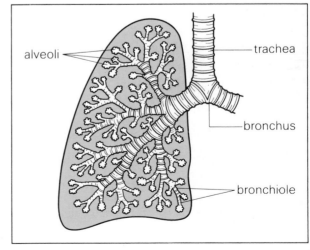

alveoli

trachea

bronchus

bronchiole

*The lungs are made up of tiny air sacs (like balloons) called **alveoli**. There are about 150 million alveoli in each human lung.*

What happens in the alveoli?

When you breathe in, the alveoli become full of air. There is *more* oxygen in this air than there is in the blood. The oxygen can therefore diffuse from a region of high concentration (in the alveoli) to a region of low concentration (in the blood). In order to make this process efficient, the walls of the alveoli are very thin. Small molecules, such as oxygen, can pass through these walls. The inner lining of the walls are covered by a thin layer of water. The oxygen has to dissolve in the water then diffuse through the walls in order to pass into the blood.

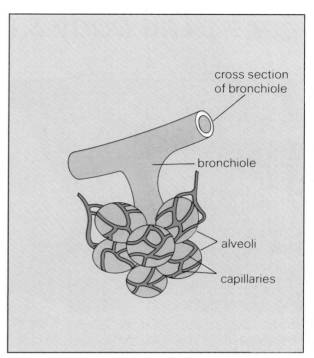

Oxygen diffuses out through the walls of the alveoli into blood vessels called capillaries.

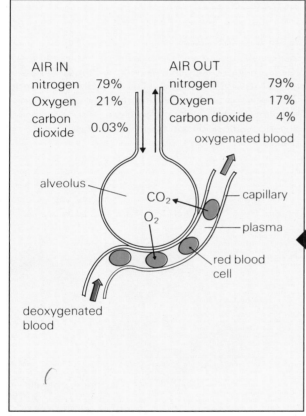

AIR IN		AIR OUT	
nitrogen	79%	nitrogen	79%
Oxygen	21%	Oxygen	17%
carbon dioxide	0.03%	carbon dioxide	4%

Carbon dioxide diffuses from the blood into the alveoli. Oxygen combines with haemoglobin found in red blood cells.

What happens in the blood?

In order to make the uptake of oxygen by the blood very efficient, it is contained in blood vessels, with very thin walls, called capillaries. The capillaries criss-cross the outer wall of each alveolus so that a large amount of blood is available for the oxygen to diffuse into. In the blood, there are red blood cells which contain a substance called **haemoglobin**. Haemoglobin is very efficient at combining with the oxygen (*see 3.9*).

The carbon dioxide is dissolved in the liquid part of the blood called **plasma** which contains mainly water. Blood flowing into the lungs and through the alveoli will contain a lot of carbon dioxide that the body has produced during respiration. The air in the alveoli will contain very little carbon dioxide. Carbon dioxide will, therefore, diffuse from the blood into the alveoli.

1.
   a What is diffusion?
   b Give two other examples of diffusion.
   c Does diffusion in the lungs take place in air or in water?

2. Why are the lungs made of millions of tiny balloons and not one?

3. Why does diffusion only take place in the alveoli and not in the bronchiole or trachea?

4. State two features of the capillaries which enable the blood in them to take in a large amount of oxygen.

5. In a 100 cm^3 of blood, there is 55 cm^3 of carbon dioxide entering the lungs and 50 cm^3 leaving. If the amount of blood flowing into the lungs in 1 minute is 5 litres, how much carbon dioxide enters the alveoli in that time?

6. Describe the path of carbon dioxide from the blood into the air.

3.9   The body's transport system

Blood is carried through your body, along capillaries (magnified here × 1200) taking food and oxygen to all your cells.

Life blood

Your body is constantly taking in useful substances such as oxygen and food – essential to life. Once these substances have been absorbed by the lungs and by the small intestine they need to be distributed all around the body. The distribution of food and oxygen to all the body's cells is carried out by **blood** – the body's transport system. As well as carrying useful substances the blood also carries waste materials away from cells.

What is blood made of?

When you cut yourself the blood which flows out looks like a red liquid. But blood is really a mixture of **red** and **white cells** in a pale yellow liquid called **plasma.** This liquid part of blood is largely water with a large number of substances dissolved in it, e.g. salts, sugars, amino acids and waste substances such as urea.

Red blood cells

Blood contains a huge number of red blood cells – every 1 cm³ of blood contains about 5000 million red cells! Red blood cells contain a substance called **haemoglobin** which gives blood its deep red colour. The job of haemoglobin is to carry oxygen around the body. Haemoglobin contains iron which plays an important part in the way oxygen is transported. The iron in haemoglobin combines with oxygen in the lungs to form **oxyhaemoglobin.** The blood flowing out of the lungs carries the oxyhaemoglobin to all parts of the body. This is why we need iron in our diet.

Red blood cells have a very distinctive shape. They are like discs which have been pressed in on both sides. This shape gives a red blood cell a greater surface area over which to take up oxygen.

White blood cells

White blood cells are larger and fewer than red blood cells. There is approximately one white cell for every 700 red cells. They have a nucleus just like most cells. Their job is to fight infection and disease. Some types of white cells (phagocytes) can digest and destroy bacteria. Other types (lymph cells) produce special chemicals called **antibodies** which enable the body to resist infection. Antibodies are produced by the lymph cells when germs enter your body.

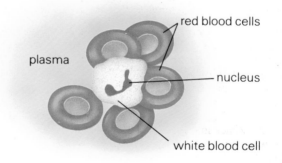

cross-section of red blood cell

Human blood is made up of red cells, white cells and plasma. Red cells have a distinctive disc-like shape.

Blood vessels

Blood is carried around the body in small tubes called blood vessels. Blood inside these vessels is kept moving by the pumping action of the heart. Blood vessels which carry blood away from the heart are called **arteries.** Those carrying blood back to the heart are called **veins.** The very small blood vessels which link arteries and veins are called **capillaries.** The walls of capillaries are very thin so that substances can be exchanged between blood and body cells.

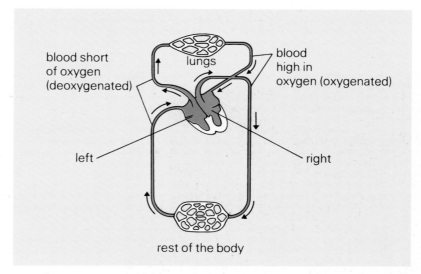

A general view of the human blood circulatory system showing the double pump action of the heart.

Pumping the system

The heart is the blood system's pump. The pumping action is brought about by the thick muscular walls of the heart. If you look at the diagram opposite you can see that the heart is really a double pump. One side of the heart (the right hand side) pumps blood (deoxygenated) through the lungs. The other side (the left hand side) pumps freshly oxygenated blood that comes from the lungs to the rest of the body.

From the diagram of its detailed structure you can see that the heart is divided into four chambers. Each side is divided into an upper part called an **atrium,** and a lower part called a **ventricle.** There are valves at the entrances to each of the four chambers in the heart. The heart valves only allow blood to flow in one direction, e.g. when the ventricles contract no blood can flow back into the atria because the valves between them close. The sort of "lubb dup" sound that the heart makes as it beats is made as the valves snap shut.

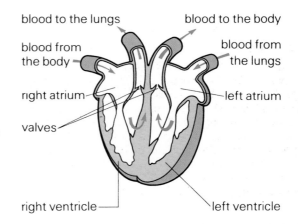

The valves prevent the blood from flowing backwards. The arrows show the direction of the blood (blue – deoxygenated; red – oxygenated) through the heart.

1 What is the role of a) white blood cells, and b) plasma?

2 **a** Where in the body is oxyhaemoglobin formed?
  b A shortage of iron in the diet can cause anaemia – a disorder which causes people to become pale and tired. Why does this happen?

3 Arteries, veins and capillaries do different jobs. What are they?

4 What prevents blood flowing back into the atria when the ventricles contract?

5 List, in order, the parts of the blood transport system that blood flows through after it enters the heart and then leaves the heart to go to the rest of the body.

6 The **blood pressure** of a healthy adult is about 120/70. Why do you think there are two measurements given and what do you think each indicates?

3.10 *Making the body work hard*

Measurements of breathing rate and heart beat, when subject is first at rest and then after hard exercise.

What happens when you work hard?

The people in the photograph are working hard to win the table tennis match! They are pushing their bodies hard and as they do so they start to pant and sweat. If their pulse was measured it would probably be faster than normal. Why do all these changes take place?

Releasing enough energy

When you work hard your muscles need more energy – energy that is released from glucose. During respiration in muscle cells, glucose is combined with oxygen and carbon dioxide, water and energy are released. The energy that is released is used by muscles to move your body. More respiration takes place to release more energy when muscle cells are made to work harder. This uses up large amounts glucose and oxygen. The degree of work that you can expect from your muscles depends on how fast your body can supply glucose and oxygen. The table below shows some of the changes that take place in your body during strenous exercise.

	Number of breaths per min	Volume of each breath (cm³)	Pulse beats per min	Volume of blood leaving the heart after each beat (cm³)
At rest	18	450	72	65
After 10 mins strenuous exercise	41	1050	90	120

Rate of blood flow in cm³ per min

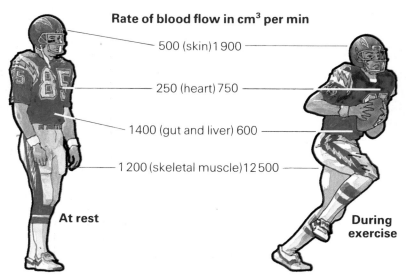

- 500 (skin) 1 900
- 250 (heart) 750
- 1400 (gut and liver) 600
- 1 200 (skeletal muscle) 12 500

At rest

During exercise

The rate of blood flowing to the main regions of the body increases as you work harder.

Getting in supplies

By breathing faster and deeper as you work harder you take in more air. Over five times more air is breathed in to the lungs during hard physical activity. Your heart also beats faster and harder to pump blood around the body faster so that hard working muscles obtain more oxygen and glucose, and waste carbon dioxide is removed. These are not the only changes that take place in your body during exercise. The amount of blood flowing to various parts of the body also changes.

Stopping the body over-heating

The table opposite shows that the volume of blood flowing to the heart, muscles and skin increases during physical activity. The increased flow of blood to the heart and muscle provides more oxygen and glucose to hard working muscles, but why is there more blood flowing through the skin? Some of the energy released during respiration is released as heat. The bloodstream carries this waste heat away from muscle to the skin surface. This is why some people go red during exercise. As blood flows through the skin heat is lost to the air which prevents the body temperature increasing to a dangerous level. This is also why you sweat as you exercise. The body is cooled because heat is taken from the skin as drops of sweat evaporate (*see 3.17*).

Getting tired

Your body can become short of oxygen during strenuous exercise even though you breathe faster and deeper and your heart works harder. This is because your muscles will be using oxygen faster than it is supplied. When this happens some glucose is broken down without using oxygen. This is anaeobic respiration. (You can find out more about this process on spread 3.7.) A harmful substance called lactic acid is produced as a waste product. As lactic acid builds up it slows muscles down, and they will stop working altogether if a lot of lactic acid is produced.

This woman's face is looking red because she is exerting herself. This shows that there is more blood flowing through her skin, carrying waste heat away.

After a sudden burst of activity, during which anaerobic respiration would be required, it takes some time before breathing returns to 'normal'.

Getting into debt

People continue to breathe heavily after exercising hard, even though they have finished exercising. This is because oxygen is needed to change lactic acid to harmless substances. This extra amount of oxygen that is required is called the **oxygen debt**. Some athletes build up an oxygen debt of 17 litres and it may take up to an hour before their breathing gets back to normal.

fast running

Time in minutes	0	10	20	30	40	50	60	70	80
Relative amount of lactic acid in blood	2	2	12	8	6	4	3	2	2

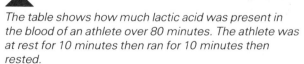

The table shows how much lactic acid was present in the blood of an athlete over 80 minutes. The athlete was at rest for 10 minutes then ran for 10 minutes then rested.

1. a Use the information in the table on the opposite page to identify *four* changes that take place in the body during exercise.
    b How much extra air is breathed into the lungs each minute during exercise?
    c How much blood leaves the heart each minute at rest and during exercise?

2. Study the diagram on the opposite page, showing changes in the rate of blood flow.
    a Which parts of the body show an increased blood flow during exercise?
    b Use the data to explain why it is bad to exercise after a meal?

3.11 *Fit for life*

Fit for what?

Many people spend time jogging, going to aerobics classes or to the local health club trying to get and stay fit. But what is fitness? Professional sportspeople need to be very fit to compete against others in their sport. They work very hard at improving their overall fitness. But everyone needs to be fit enough to carry out everyday activities such as mowing the lawn or carrying the shopping! Becoming tired and short of breath after climbing a few flights of stairs or lacking the energy to walk to the local shops are signs of being unfit and unhealthy. Do you think you maybe unfit?

Fitness isn't just a measure of whether you can win an olympic medal! We all need to be fit to go about our daily activities – like doing the shopping! ▲

This table shows the effects of regular exercise on the body. (All measurements are taken when the person is at rest).

▼

	Before getting fit	After becoming fit
Amount of blood pumped out of the heart during each beat (cm³)	64	80
Heart volume (cm³)	120	140
Breathing rate (no. of breaths per min.)	14	12
Pulse rate	72	63

Improving fitness

Exercising regularly improves your fitness. Any activity which gives you exercise is good for you. This is because exercise has several effects on the body. When you exercise regularly:

- your muscles become larger and able to work longer and harder.
- your heart muscle becomes stronger so that the blood is pumped around the body more efficiently.
- your breathing becomes more efficient and more air can be taken in with each breath.
- the risk of heart attacks and strokes decreases because of the improved circulation.

Effects of exercise

Some of these effects of regular exercise on the body can be seen in the table opposite. The measurements shown in the table are taken from the same person before and after several months of regular exercise. The **pulse** rate in the table indicates the rate of heart beat. You can usually feel a pulse rate on your wrist fairly easily. This pulse is the swelling of arteries as your heart forces blood through them. Each pulse is the result of each beat of your heart.

Using pulse rates

You can see from the previous table that the resting pulse rate *decreased* as the person became fitter. In a fit person the pulse rate is often low. It increases during exercise and then it rapidly returns to normal. In an unfit person exercise makes the pulse rate go very high and it returns to normal only slowly. Measuring pulse rate before and after exercise is a good way to assess fitness because it indicates the efficiency of the heart and circulation.

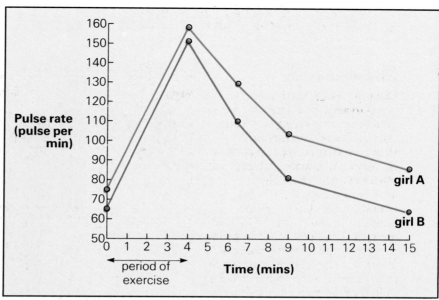

This graph shows the pulse rates of two girls. Can you tell who is the fittest?

Stamina to keep going

The ability of your breathing system and lungs to supply oxygen and remove carbon dioxide is an important part of fitness. A good supply of oxygen improves stamina or "staying power" so that you can keep running or walking without getting tired and puffed out.

The breathing rate and the volume of air taken in by a person during each breath can be measured using a **spirometer.** A trace is produced which shows the pattern of breathing and the amount of air taken in by the person being monitored.

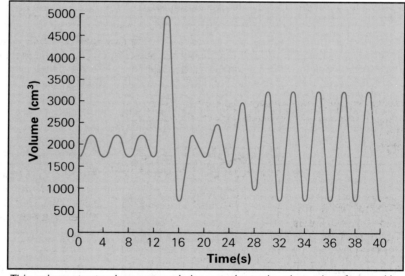

This spirometer tracing was made by a student who plays a lot of sport. He was asked to breathe steadily at rest, then to breathe in and out as deeply as possible and finally to breathe steadily while exercising.

1. What effect does exercise have on
   a the size of the heart, and
   b the strength of heart beat?
   Explain your answer.

2. "Fitness makes breathing more efficient so that more air can be taken in with each breath." What evidence is there in the table opposite to support this statement

3. a Use the graph of pulse rates to suggest which girl is the fitter.
   b Give *two* reasons for your choice

4. Use the spirometer trace above to calculate:
   a how much *extra* air is taken in with each breath during exercise.
   b the total amount of air that can be breathed into the lungs.

5. If a spirometer was used to measure the total volume of air that could be breathed in by a student who hardly ever takes exercise, how would the results differ from those shown here? Explain your answer.

3.12 *Dying for a smoke*

Self-inflicted disease

People's health can be affected in many ways. You may be unlucky and develop a disease or have an accident which causes serious harm. Many people in Britain become unhealthy and die unnecessarily young from self-inflicted diseases which are entirely avoidable. Cigarette smoking is the main *preventable* cause of death in Britain.

Evidence of the dangers of smoking

Doctors have been treating people with lung diseases for many years. From the evidence of medical records, doctors became aware of a link between lung cancer and other lung diseases and smoking. In other words they made the hypothesis that:

> **People who smoke are more likely to develop lung cancer and other lung diseases than those who don't.**

Many surveys have been carried out to test this hypothesis. Here are just two examples: ▼

The dangers of smoking have been well known for more than twenty years but recent surveys show that almost half of the adult population continue to smoke.

SURVEY 1

A survey was made of the 280 people born in one city during one week in 1940. By Jan 1987, 25 of these were suffering from, or had died of, lung cancer. 30 had died from other causes. Of the 25 with lung cancer, 20 were smokers, 5 were not. Of those who did not have lung cancer, 95 were smokers, 130 were not.

SURVEY 2

One of the most detailed investigations of the effects of smoking involved making a record of the smoking habits and health records of thousands of people over a period of 22 years. The results of this investigation are shown in the two graphs below.

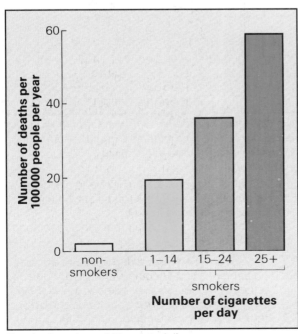

Deaths from bronchitis related diseases.

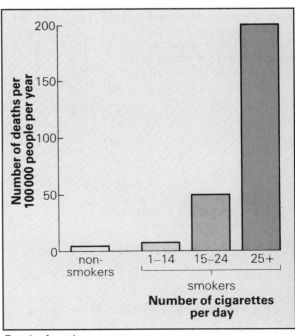

Deaths from lung cancer.

Damaging the air passages

When someone smokes a cigarette four harmful substances are inhaled. Nicotine, hydrocarbon tars, carbon monoxide and dust particles enter the air passages and lungs of the smoker. The lining of the air passages to the lungs, the trachea and the bronchi, traps any dust particles and bacteria which are taken in with inhaled air. The tar in cigarette smoke damages the lining making the trachea and bronchi become red and sore. This causes persistent coughing and shortness of breath – the typical 'smoker's cough' or bronchitis which may worsen enough to cripple the smoker.

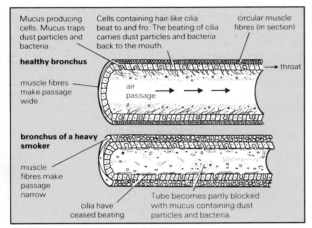

Smoking causes severe damage to the bronchus.

Damaging the lungs

The damage to the air passages eventually leads to bacteria, mucus, dust particles and tar building up in the lungs. This can result in **emphysema** – a condition in which the walls of the alveoli break down so reducing the surface area for gas exchange. The tar can also cause the cells in the lungs to grow in an uncontrolled way. This is cancer – the formation of tumours which can be fatal. Less than 5% of the people who get lung cancer are alive after five years. Britain has the highest lung cancer death rate in the world.

Substance in cigarette smoke	Damage to the body
Tar	Stops the lining of air passages working. Lung cancer.
Nicotine	Narrows arteries which increases blood pressure and risk of heart attack.
Carbon monoxide (CO)	Reduces the blood's ability to carry oxygen. Heart attacks are more likely because this makes the heart work harder.
Dust particles	Irritates the lining of the bronchi and damages the walls of the alveoli.

This table gives details of the damage caused by the four main harmful substances in cigarette smoke.

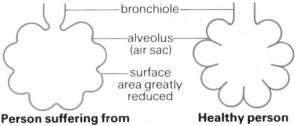

Person suffering from emphysema   **Healthy person**

A person with emphysema gets very short of breath because the surface area over which gas exchange takes place is severely reduced (see 3.8).

Other serious effects of smoking

Smoking is also associated with an increased risk of heart disease and possibly other cancers – mouth, throat, oesophagus and bladder. Also a woman who smokes while she is pregnant may cause damage to the unborn foetus she is carrying.

---

1   **a**   Name three respiratory diseases caused by cigarette smoke.
    b   Do the results of survey 1 support the hypothesis that people who smoke are more likely to develop lung disease? Explain why?

2   **a**   Make a table to summarise the results of survey 2.
    b   One person in this survey said, "My uncle Jimmy smokes like a chimney and he's 84, so smoking won't do me any harm." Does the evidence from survey 2 agree with this view? Explain your answer.

3   **a**   What is the function of an alveolus?
    b   Describe the difference, which can be seen in the diagram above, between a healthy lung and a lung with emphysema.
    c   Explain how this affects how well the lung works.

4   **a**   Name *two* substances in cigarette smoke that can lead to heart disease.
    b   Explain the effect each of these substances has on the body and why they increase the risk of heart attacks.

3.13 Removing the body's waste

Getting rid of harmful waste

A large number of chemical reactions take place inside your body to keep you alive. The waste products of some reactions are poisonous and must be removed from the body. **Excretion** is the process which removes the waste products of the body's chemical reactions. All excretory substances are formed from chemical reactions. Carbon dioxide and water are products of respiration, and urea is a product of the breakdown of amino acids. Some substances such as the roughage in your diet are not digested or absorbed and so do not become part of the chemical reactions going on inside you. The removal of undigested food (egestion) is carried out by the process of **defaecation** (see 3.6).

Excreting waste from protein

Protein in your diet is digested into amino acids and then absorbed into the bloodstream. Some amino acids will be used to make the protein needed for growth. Amino acids which are not used to make new protein will be broken down by the process of **deamination** in the liver. This process produces **urea** as an excretory product which is then filtered from the blood by the kidneys.

Waste product	How the product is formed	Excretory organ
carbon dioxide	respiration in all living cells	lungs
water	respiration in all living cells and from food	lungs kidneys
urea	deamination in the liver	kidneys

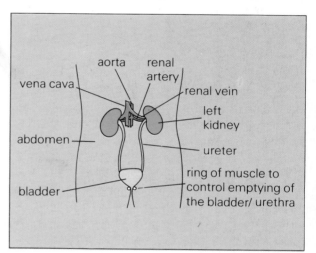

The position of the kidneys in the body. Blood flows into each kidney along a renal artery and leaves along a renal vein.

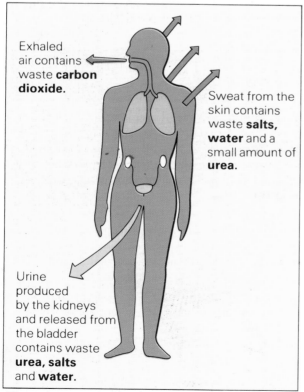

The main excretory substances formed by your body are removed by different parts of the body.

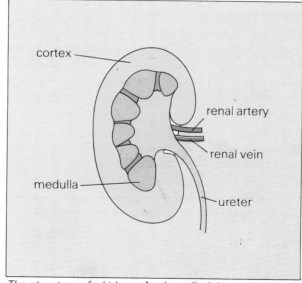

The structure of a kidney. A tube called the **ureter** runs from each kidney to the bladder.

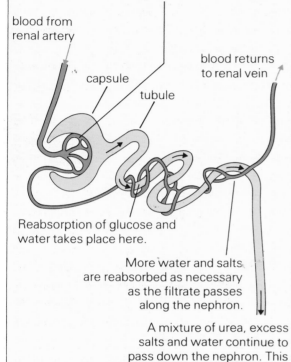

Glomerulus – first part of filtration takes place here. Blood reaching the glomerulus is under high pressure forcing the fluid part through the capillary walls, into the capsule. Large molecules – blood cells, proteins – are too big and remain in the capillaries. The filtered fluid contains small molecules – urea, glucose, water and salts.

blood from renal artery

capsule

tubule

blood returns to renal vein

Reabsorption of glucose and water takes place here.

More water and salts are reabsorbed as necessary as the filtrate passes along the nephron.

A mixture of urea, excess salts and water continue to pass down the nephron. This mixture, called **urine**, passes down the ureter to the bladder.

The structure of one nephron. Each kidney contains about a million nephrons in which filtration takes place. The kidneys work by first filtering the blood and then selectively reabsorbing into it the substances e.g. glucose and water which your body needs. The kidney can adjust the amount of water it reabsorbs according to circumstances.

Filtering out waste substances

Microscopic observation of the kidney cortex reveals thousands of very thin structures called nephrons and large numbers of knots of blood capillaries. Each knot of capillaries, called a **glomerulus,** lies at the beginning of a nephron. The glomerulus and the nephron are important in filtering waste material from blood.

The excretion of waste substances by the kidney involves two main stages. Firstly, filtration takes place as the high blood pressure in the glomerulus forces fluids out of the blood. The wall of the glomerulus and the nephron act like a filter allowing only molecules which are small enough to pass through. The filtrate passing into the tubule in the nephron is water plus soluble substances. Secondly, substances which are needed by the body are reabsorbed as the filtrate passes along the remaining part of the nephron.

You can see how important the role of the kidneys are in keeping your body alive. Together with the lungs they play a vital role in getting rid of waste materials produced in your body.

Comparison of plasma and urine

The table contains information about the amounts of various substances present in blood plasma, the filtrate in the kidney nephron and in urine. Use the table to answer questions **1** and **2** below.

| Substances | Contents in grams per 100 cm³ | | |
	Plasma	Filtrate in nephron	Urine
water	93	93	95
urea	0.02	0.02	2.0
various salts	0.4	0.4	1.18
protein	6.8	0	0
glucose	0.1	0.1	0

1 **a** Which substance is not filtered from the glomerulus into the remaining part of the kidney nephron?
  b Explain why this substance remains in the blood capillaries yet other substances are filtered.

2 **a** Name a substance present in the filtrate in the nephron but not in urine.
  b Explain what happens to this substance.

3 The table below shows the difference in the concentration of some of the substances in the blood in the renal artery and in the renal vein. Explain why each of those substances changes as blood flows through the kidney.

	renal artery	renal vein
oxygen	high	low
carbon dioxide	low	high
glucose	high	low
urea	high	low

3.14 *Cleaning the bloodstream*

Removing the body's waste

Like any other organism, you need to get rid of waste which is produced from the necessary chemical reactions that take place to keep your body alive. Your main organs for this process of waste removal called **excretion** are your lungs and kidneys. Your *lungs* remove **carbon dioxide** which is produced in respiration. Your *kidneys* remove **urea** which is formed when amino acids are broken down in the liver. Your kidneys also remove any excess water and salts taken in in your diet, and remove any foreign substances in the blood such as drugs and alcohol.

Within each of your kidneys there are thousands of tiny blood vessels (like this one) from which waste substances are filtered from the blood. ▶

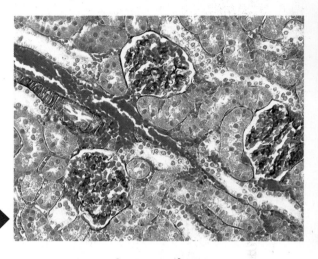

Saving and removing

Each of your kidneys contains between one and two million tiny tubes called **nephrons**. At the end of each nephron is a small cup-shaped capsule, called **Bowman's capsule** which contains a knot of capillaries called a **glomerulus**. This detailed network of the kidneys acts both to *filter* off waste substances, and to *reabsorb* important substances back into your blood. Your kidneys provide some very important functions in your body.

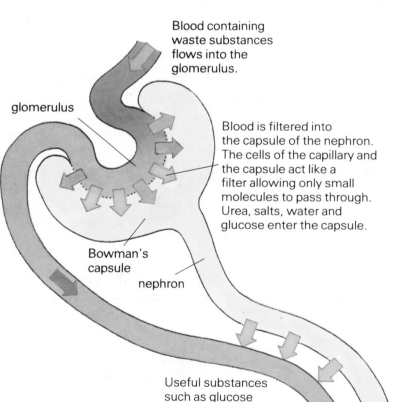

Blood containing waste substances flows into the glomerulus.

glomerulus

Blood is filtered into the capsule of the nephron. The cells of the capillary and the capsule act like a filter allowing only small molecules to pass through. Urea, salts, water and glucose enter the capsule.

Bowman's capsule

nephron

Useful substances such as glucose are absorbed back into the blood.

Cleaned blood flows back to the rest of the body.

Urine containing unwanted substances flows on to the ureter and bladder.

YOU CAN READ MORE ABOUT HOW YOUR KIDNEYS WORK ON SPREAD 3.13

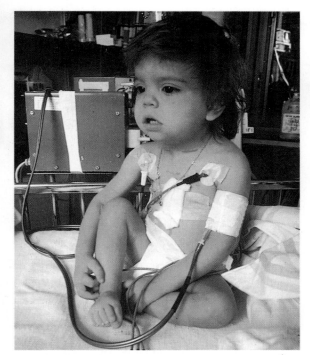

An artificial kidney – a dialysis machine – can be
a life saver for some.

Dialysis works by imitating the processes of filtration
which go on in healthy kidneys.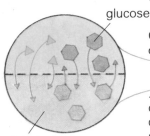

Kidney failure

Accidents, disease, drugs and alcohol abuse damage
the kidneys' ability to function properly. Until
recently, you would die if both kidneys completely
failed. However, it is now possible to use a **dialysis
machine** to do the job of the kidneys. Alternatively,
some people are able to have a kidney **transplant** –
when one kidney is transplanted from a matching
donor.

■ Why do you think a person is only given one kidney
in a transplant?

Medical machinery

A kidney machine works by removing waste
substances from the blood of the patient across an
artificial **dialysis membrane**. This membrane is
semi-permeable – it allows only *small* molecules to
pass through it. The membrane is surrounded by a
solution, called the **dialysis fluid**. The *concentration*
of substances in the dialysis fluid controls the
necessary diffusion of urea out of the blood – and the
diffusion of useful substances back in!

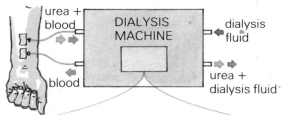

The high concentration of urea in the blood causes
urea to diffuse into the dialysis fluid

glucose

Glucose will diffuse
out of blood, but . . .

. . . dialysis fluid also
contains glucose which
diffuses back at the
same rate

dialysis fluid

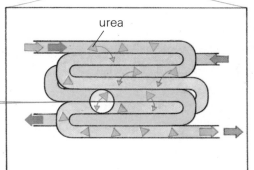

urea

1.
a Name one substance that is filtered into
the nephron and is then reabsorbed into
the blood.
b Explain why proteins are not filtered from
the blood into the glomerulus.

2. Explain why the concentration of glucose in
dialysis fluid is the same as in healthy blood.

3. State *one* way in which the working of a
kidney machine:
a is similar to a natural kidney;
b is different from a natural kidney.

4. A firm is making some new dialysis tubing.
You are the firm's chemist and have to find
out if the new tubing is permeable to urea at
body temperature (37°C).

You are provided with: ordinary laboratory
equipment; the new tubing; urea solution;
colourless dye (turns blue when mixed with
urea).

Use a diagram to show how you would carry
out your investigation.

What result would show that urea can pass
through the tubing?

3.15 *Internal control*

Controlling conditions

There are many reactions taking place in the cells of all living plants and animals to keep them alive. All of these reactions are controlled by **enzymes** – biological catalysts which enable the chemical reactions (known as the body's **metabolism**) to take place. Any slight change (in the temperature, pH level or water content of a cell) can slow down or even stop an enzyme from working. It is therefore necessary to keep the conditions inside cells as steady as possible, so that enzymes can keep the organism working at an efficient metabolic rate.

Maintaining steady conditions inside the body is called **homeostasis**. The diagram opposite shows the major organs which regulate the conditions *inside the human body*. The **brain** has overall control of homeostatic processes. The temperature and the concentration of substances in the blood are checked as blood flows through the brain. If there needs to be any change, information will be sent to the relevant body organs along **nerves** – or by releasing chemicals called **hormones** into the bloodstream.

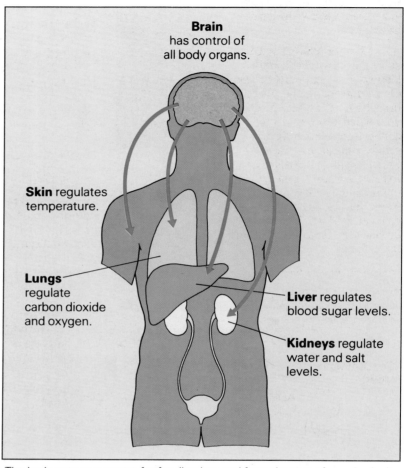

Brain has control of all body organs.

Skin regulates temperature.

Lungs regulate carbon dioxide and oxygen.

Liver regulates blood sugar levels.

Kidneys regulate water and salt levels.

The brain acts as a centre for feedback to and from the rest of your body. It receives information – say that you are hot – and activates processes to cool your body.

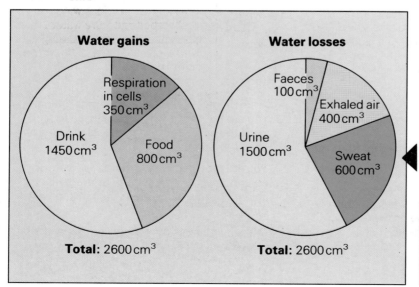

Water gains

Respiration in cells 350 cm³

Drink 1450 cm³

Food 800 cm³

Total: 2600 cm³

Water losses

Faeces 100 cm³

Exhaled air 400 cm³

Urine 1500 cm³

Sweat 600 cm³

Total: 2600 cm³

Balancing water content

You take in (and lose) water in large amounts every day. To keep the amount of water in your body at a steady level the quantity of water you drink must be balanced by the quantity that you lost through sweating, urinating etc. These two pie charts show the typical daily water balance in the human body.

The amount of water lost by the different methods shown in the pie chart will change during very hot weather. Can you predict what these changes will be?

Kidneys as regulators

You will have noticed what happens when you drink more fluid than you need to – you urinate more than usual. Why does this happen?

As well as removing waste substances (see 3.14), your kidneys also regulate the amount of water in your blood. When you drink large quantities of fluids, your blood becomes diluted – *less* concentrated. Your kidneys remove this excess water by producing *large* quantities of urine to restore water balance. On the other hand, when you are short of water your blood becomes *more* concentrated, so the kidneys produce *less* urine to conserve body water.

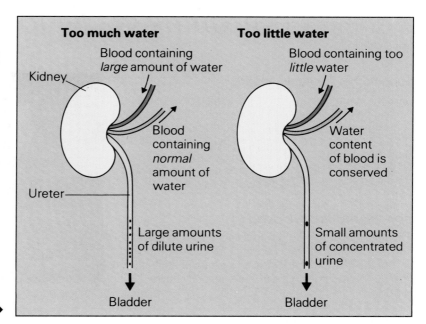

Too much water

Blood containing *large* amount of water

Kidney

Blood containing *normal* amount of water

Ureter

Large amounts of dilute urine

Bladder

Too little water

Blood containing too *little* water

Water content of blood is conserved

Small amounts of concentrated urine

Bladder

BRAIN

ADH

Concentrated blood

ADH in bloodstream

Most water is absorbed back into blood

Concentrated urine (*small* amount)

BRAIN

Dilute blood

No ADH in bloodstream

Little water is absorbed back into blood

Dilute urine (*large* amount)

Chemical control

The amount of water you lose in your urine is controlled by a hormone called the **antidiuretic hormone (ADH** for short). ADH is made by a gland in your brain and it is released when your body becomes short of water and your blood becomes concentrated. The hormone makes the wall of the kidney nephron *more porous* – so water can be reabsorbed back into your blood. *Less* water then passes in urine to your bladder. If you drink a lot of fluid, however, ADH will not be released because your blood will be quite dilute. In the *absence* of ADH, less water is reabsorbed and *more* water is present in your urine passing to the bladder – hence all those trips to the toilet!

ADH is one of the many hormones your body produces to maintain its steady state. ADH controls the amount of water removed from the body.

1 **a** State four ways in which the human body loses water.
   b Why does respiration cause an increase in the water content of the body?

2 Explain the effect that you think each of the following will have on the amount of urine produced:
   a drinking a large amount of fruit juice.
   b cold weather.
   c long periods of vigorous exercise.
   d damage to the gland that produces ADH.

YOU CAN READ MORE ABOUT CONTROLLING THE BODY ON SPREAD 3.18.

3.16 Controlling water loss in plants

Good homes for young plants

Gardeners often keep cuttings healthy by enclosing them in polythene bags or by using specially designed **propogators**. This ensures that the cuttings are provided with a warm and humid environment with plenty of sunlight – ideal conditions for successful growth. A humid environment is essential because the cuttings will soon die if they begin to dry out.

Plants will soon die if they dry out.

How do cuttings lose water?

The following investigation was carried out to find out how water was lost from cuttings. To find out which part of the leaf water is lost from a group of students designed and carried out the investigation shown below.

Three fresh sycamore leaves were treated as follows:

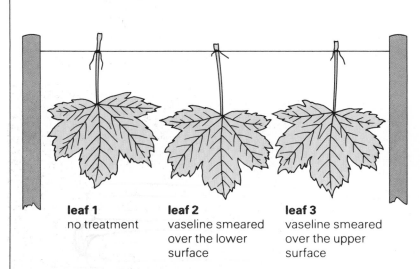

leaf 1
no treatment

leaf 2
vaseline smeared over the lower surface

leaf 3
vaseline smeared over the upper surface

Time	Loss of mass (in mg)		
	leaf 1	leaf 2	leaf 3
30 mins	10	3	11
60 mins	19	11	18
90 mins	26	19	27
120 mins	44	25	41

The leaves were left hanging from string in the laboratory. Each one was weighed at 30 minute intervals.

The students made the conclusion that most water is lost from the lower surface of leaves. Do you agree with their conclusion?

How is water lost from the leaf surface?

The students wanted to find out why most water is lost from the lower surface. They observed that the leaves they were using had a shiny upper surface and a much duller lower surface. They then carried out a series of observations using a microscope. They looked at a thin section through a leaf and then they looked at the upper and lower layer of the leaf after it had been carefully peeled away. All their observations are shown in the diagrams on the page opposite. What do these observations tell you about how water is lost from a leaf?

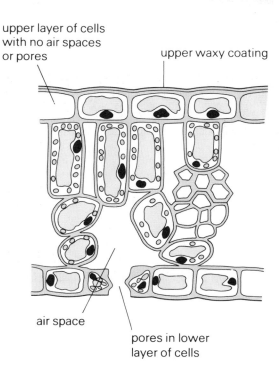

upper layer of cells with no air spaces or pores

upper waxy coating

air space

pores in lower layer of cells

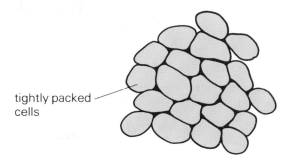

tightly packed cells

View of upper surface of leaf

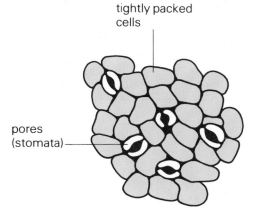

tightly packed cells

pores (stomata)

View of lower surface of leaf

Controlling water loss

The pores in leaves can open and close. During the day the pores are usually open to allow large amounts of carbon dioxide to enter the leaf for photosynthesis. During the night the pores are closed. Some plants can close their pores when water loss is high to prevent water being lost faster than it is absorbed by roots. Plants have developed many different features in their leaves to prevent too much water being lost.

Reducing the size of leaves helps to reduce water loss.

 1

  a Which leaf in the investigation shows the greatest loss in mass?

  b Use the observations on leaf structure to explain why most water is lost from this surface.

  c Suggest two improvements that could be made to improve the design of the investigation.

2 Cobalt chloride paper is blue when it is dry and pink when wet. A student attached a strip of cobalt chloride paper to two leaves using cellotape. One was attached to the upper surface and the other to the lower surface. The student observed the leaves every 30 minutes.

Predict how the paper on each leaf will change. Will the result be the same for both leaves? Explain your answer.

3.17 *Keeping warm and staying cool*

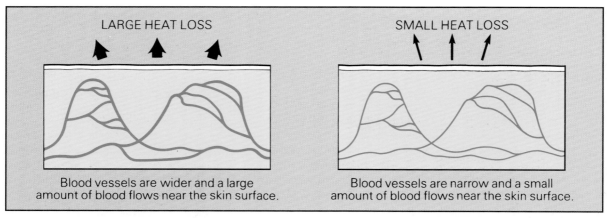

LARGE HEAT LOSS	SMALL HEAT LOSS
Blood vessels are wider and a large amount of blood flows near the skin surface.	Blood vessels are narrow and a small amount of blood flows near the skin surface.

Your blood vessels widen as your body temperature rises . . . . .

. . and then narrow as it cools down.

This bar chart shows the amount of sweat produced by four people on a beach on a very hot day. Why is there such a difference between them? ▼

Controlling body temperature

The temperature inside your body remains at about 37°C even when you are lazing in the hot sun or waiting for the school bus on a cold winter's morning. By keeping your body temperature the same you can remain reasonably active at all times throughout the year. Some animals e.g. the lizard, which cannot keep a constant body temperature, become inactive when there is a low temperature around them. Their body temperature becomes too low to maintain all the chemical reactions needed to release energy for movement.

When your body temperature begins to rise the blood vessels (**arterioles**) near the skin surface become wider allowing more blood to flow through them (**vasodilation**). This is what makes you become red in the face during strenuous activity. As warm blood flows through the skin it becomes cooler as heat is lost.

To prevent you losing heat in cold weather, the blood vessels near the skin surface become narrower so less blood can flow through them (**vaso-constriction**). This keeps the warm blood away from the skin surface so that little body heat is lost.

Stay cool!

When you become hot your body releases sweat onto the skin surface from sweat glands. As this layer of sweat evaporates it takes heat from your body and so cools it down. The hotter you become the more you sweat. Sweating virtually stops in cold weather as you no longer need to cool your body down.

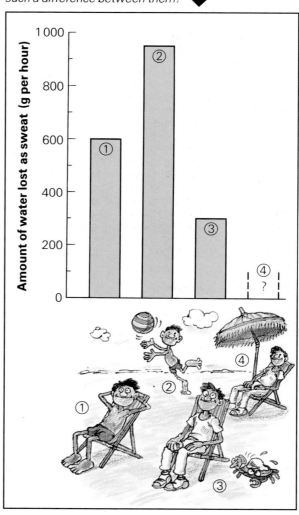

. . . but not cold!

It is just as important that your body does not become too cold, as well as too warm. **Hypothermia** is a gradual cooling of the body until, even deep inside, the temperature is below the normal 37°C. At about 2°C below normal 37°C, the central control of the brain begins to be affected – body movements and speech become slow and the person becomes drowsy and will eventually go into a coma. Death can occur if no action is taken to increase the body temperature. Old people and babies are especially vulnerable to hypothermia as are people who are exposed to severe damp and wind – pot holers, hikers etc.

This woman needs to make sure that the temperature of the room in which she is sitting is above 20°C, otherwise her body temperature may begin to drop. ▼

Thousands die from hypothermia

"Its, a national disgrace," says Labour M.P. Tony Lancaster to-day. "As soon as we get a prolonged cold spell thousands of old people die of hypothermia. Every such death is unnecessary! We should judge this government by the way it treats its old, its young and the disabled."

Cold kills the old

Joan Rogers, a community nurse explains why old people are especially vulnerable to hypothermia. "They need to rest more and so they make less heat from their muscles. Old people often have poor circulation and so they cannot distribute heat around their body." She adds, "Many old people are underweight because they have difficulty getting to the shops to buy food. This means that they don't eat enough food to produce the heat energy they desperately need. The problem is made worse because hypothermia slows down mental processes and victims don't realize what is happening to them."

Body temperature

38	– Fever & sweating
37.2	– normal body temp
36	–
35	– Shivering
34	– Tiredness
33	– Sleepiness
32	– Loss of feeling
30	– COMA
28	– Breathing stops
26	–
25	– CERTAIN DEATH!!

H Y P O T H E R M I A

Caring for the old

"The old and sick are supported by a good health service" states Conservative M.P. Jill Townsend. She adds, "When cold weather is prolonged money is available for extra fuel. Leaflets have been distributed so that everyone knows how to apply for the extra cash." Community nurse Joan Rogers reckons that old people need more help applying for the money. "Many old people either don't know about the grant or don't understand how to apply for it. They try to save money by using less fuel and so their homes get very cold. If they heat one room warm at all times it will help to keep them warm. They should also wrap themselves up in extra clothing when they leave the room."

---

1 Use the information on the bar chart on the opposite page to answer the following:
  a Why is more sweat produced when playing compared to sitting in the sun?
  b Why is less sweat produced by wearing white clothes while sitting in the sun?
  c Predict how much sweat will be lost per hour by the person sitting in the shade. Explain your answer.

2 It takes 2.5 kJ of energy to evaporate 1 g of sweat. How much heat energy will be lost by evaporation in one hour by the person playing in the sun?

3 **a** Give three reasons why old people are more likely to die from hypothermia.
  b Why do people become tired and sleepy when their body temperature drops as low as 34°C?

4 Read the "newspaper article" above and list the ways that people at risk can avoid hypothermia.

3.18 *Maintaining the balance*

Life-giving fuel

All your body cells need a continuous supply of energy
to carry out the processes that keep you alive. The
main source of energy for all cells is **glucose**. All
body cells need a continuous supply of glucose to
provide them with the energy they need.

*Vigorous exercise uses up large amounts of energy
from glucose.*

Input and output

Glucose is carried around your body dissolved in blood
plasma. Every 100 cm³ of plasma contains between
80–100 mg of glucose. When you eat a meal you are
likely to take in enough carbohydrate to increase the
amount of blood glucose by 20 times. During a
kilometre run you will use up about 100 g of glucose –
enough to remove the small amount in your blood
many times over. Despite these large variations in
intake and use the amount of glucose in the blood
remains at a fairly steady level.

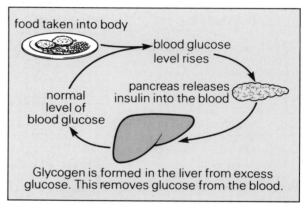

food taken into body

blood glucose
level rises

pancreas releases
insulin into the blood

normal
level of
blood glucose

Glycogen is formed in the liver from excess
glucose. This removes glucose from the blood.

*Processes in both the pancreas and the liver control the
level of glucose in the blood.*

Keeping the balance

Your body is able to maintain a steady concentration of
glucose by the action of two hormones – **insulin** and
glucagon which are secreted by the pancreas.
Maintaining a steady level of glucose is an example of
homeostasis (*see 3.15*).

After eating a meal blood sugar will increase. As the
amount of blood glucose increases the pancreas
releases **insulin** into the bloodstream. When insulin
reaches the liver it stimulates the liver cells to extract
glucose from the blood and store it as **glycogen**. The
effect of insulin is to *lower blood glucose* back to its
normal level.

During exercise the amount of blood glucose will
begin to fall as it is used during respiration. As the
amount of blood glucose falls, the pancreas releases
glucagon into the bloodstream. When glucagon
reaches the liver it stimulates the breakdown of
stored glycogen into glucose. The effect of glucagon is
to *increase blood glucose* back to its normal level.

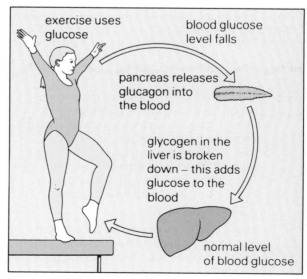

exercise uses
glucose

blood glucose
level falls

pancreas releases
glucagon into
the blood

glycogen in the
liver is broken
down – this adds
glucose to the
blood

normal level
of blood glucose

Automatic control

Changes in the amount of blood glucose trigger off hormone actions which bring the amount of glucose back to normal. An increase in the amount of blood glucose automatically triggers off reactions to lower the amount. A decrease in the amount of glucose brings about reactions to raise the amount. This effect, called **negative feedback**, is shown in the diagram opposite.

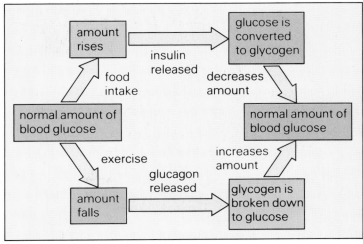

Regulating blood glucose by negative feedback.

Measuring the level of blood glucose

This table shows the amount of glucose in the blood of two people, Sumita and Jonathan, after they had each drunk a can of fruit juice containing 50 grammes of glucose. Notice how the blood glucose level changes in the two hours after drinking the juice. Jonathan has a disease called diabetes which means he is unable to produce adequate amounts of insulin. How does this disease affect his blood glucose level?

Time after drinking can of fruit juice in minutes	Blood glucose level in mg per 100 cm³ blood	
	Sumita	Jonathan
0	86	85
15	110	125
30	140	170
45	115	190
60	90	210
75	80	210
90	84	200
105	85	180
120	85	145

Daily fluctuations

The graph opposite shows how the amount of blood glucose changes during a typical day. Study the graph carefully and then answer question 1 below.

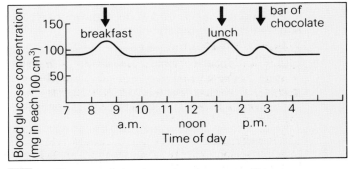

1 **a** Explain why blood glucose increases at the times shown on the graph. In your answer you need to describe the processes which take place. (You may need to refer to page 74.)
  b Explain why blood glucose does not rise over 120 mg even though lunch may contain over 100 g of glucose.

2 **a** What is meant by negative feedback?
  b Explain how the amount of glucose in the blood is controlled by this mechanism.

3 **a** Plot a graph to show the changes in the blood glucose level of Jonathan and Sumita.
  b Describe the changes that take place in Sumita's blood glucose level. Explain how these changes are brought about.
  c Use the information in your graph to explain how Jonathan is affected by diabetes.

Sensitive to change

Responding to change

Like any living organism your body is always responding to changes in your surroundings. You will start to sweat if you are too hot; shiver if you are cold. Any change in the surroundings which affects an organism is called a **stimulus**. For example, a snake will flick out its tongue as it moves around to taste chemicals in the air. The chemicals released into the air (from other animals and plants) are stimuli that snakes can detect. The snake's tongue picks up chemicals, and carries them to **receptors** in its mouth which can detect even the slightest trace of chemicals. The ability to respond to stimuli in this way is called **sensitivity.** The snake's tongue is sensitive to chemicals produced by plants and animals. It uses this to find food, and avoid being attacked by predators – a 'whiff' of life and death for the snake!

Slow to respond

Plants cannot move from place to place to find their food, but they still need to respond to changes in their surroundings. A plant growing on a window-sill will grow towards light – so that its leaves are placed in the best position for photosynthesis.

By changing the way in which its leaves (or flowers) are positioned, or by growing its shoots or roots in certain directions, a plant can make *slow* movements that respond to its environment. A change in the direction of plant growth is called a **tropism**. For example, the growth response caused by light is called a **phototropism**.

It takes a much longer time for a plant to respond to change than it does a snake.

From stimulus to response

The following sequence is a model of the events that take place when an organism responds to a stimulus:

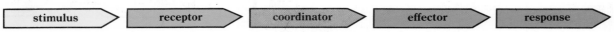

| stimulus | receptor | coordinator | effector | response |

A rapid or complex response may involve several separate actions happening together. The more rapid or complex the response, the more important the coordinator stage becomes.

Look at how the snake responds to its surroundings in this sequence:

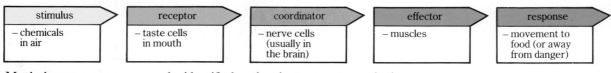

stimulus	receptor	coordinator	effector	response
– chemicals in air	– taste cells in mouth	– nerve cells (usually in the brain)	– muscles	– movement to food (or away from danger)

Much the same sequence can be identified as the plant grows towards the light:

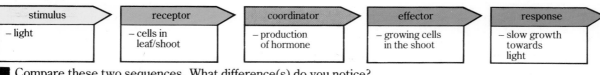

stimulus	receptor	coordinator	effector	response
– light	– cells in leaf/shoot	– production of hormone	– growing cells in the shoot	– slow growth towards light

■ Compare these two sequences. What difference(s) do you notice?
■ What explanation(s) can you give for the difference(s)?

Investigating animal behaviour

The behaviour of small animals such as woodlice can be observed using a **choice chamber.** You can look at how they respond to a particular stimulus – such as a change in humidity. In the investigation shown here, the chamber is divided into a humid (moist) side and a dry side. Some students observed that on placing 10 woodlice into a choice chamber, they immediately crawled about in all directions. When the woodlice found themselves on the dry side, they moved about rapidly. In contrast, the woodlice on the wet side moved slowly and eventually stopped. After 20 minutes of being in the chamber, 9 of the woodlice were on the wet side, and remaining there.

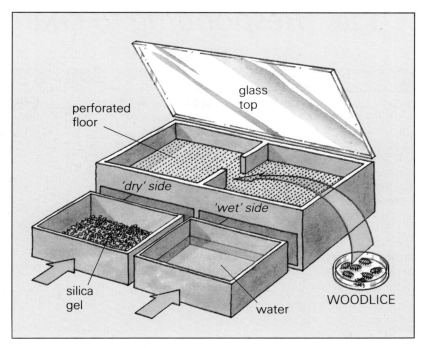

Investigating plant behaviour

The slow responses of plants to stimuli mean that observations need to last several days. Investigations, such as the three examples illustrated here, show that plants do respond to several different stimuli.

What kind of stimulus does the plant respond to in each of these three investigations? How does it respond?

What does this investigation tell you about the production of hormone and its effect on plant growth?

1
a How do woodlice respond to dry air?
b How would you make sure that the woodlice in the investigation were responding to differences in humidity?
c Where would you expect to find woodlice in the environment?

2
a Interpret the results of the investigation into plant growth shown above.
b What is the response observed in sample 1 called?
c How do you think the seedling benefits from this response?

3
When the young shoots of a bean plant are stroked lightly with a match, they coil. What is the stimulus which produces this response?

How do bean plants growing in the garden benefit from this response?

3.20 Responding to change

Stimulus	Receptor	Sense
Light energy	Light sensitive cells, called rods + cones in the retina of the eye	Vision
Sound energy	Cells in the cochlea of the ear	Hearing
Gravity e.g. falling (Movement energy)	Gravity receptors in the ear	Balance
Change in temperature (Heat energy)	Temperature receptors in the skin	Temperature detection
Pressure, pain and touch	Pressure, pain and touch receptors in the skin	Touch and pain
Chemicals in the air, drink and food (Chemical energy)	Chemical receptors in the nose and tongue	Smell and taste

Detecting change

Like many animals, you have a **nervous system** that enables your body to detect and to respond quickly to stimuli. Your **senses** make you aware of changes taking place inside your body and around you. Special sense organs contain **receptors** that detect different kinds of stimuli. A stimulus, such as bright sunlight, reaches a receptor as a form of **energy** – as light energy. Receptors convert this energy into electrical energy which travels along your **nerves** as **nerve impulses**.

You have receptors in the sense organs of your body which detect different stimuli.

Linking all parts of the body

The main parts of the nervous system are shown here. The **brain** and **spinal cord** form the **central nervous system (CNS)** which is linked to all parts of the body by a network of thousands of branching nerves. The CNS and nerves are made up of nerve cells or **neurones**. Each neurone has a cell body with long fibres spreading from it. The long nerve fibres carry impulses from one part of the body to another. Hundreds of tiny nerve fibres are bundled together to form a single nerve.

Organising the best response

When the receptors in your sense organs are stimulated, impulses are carried along **sensory neurones** to the central nervous system. Your brain or spinal cord coordinates your body's response to the stimulus by sending impulses along **motor neurones** to the part of your body that needs to react. For example, this is what happens when you accidentally touch a hot plate and then quickly pull your hand away:

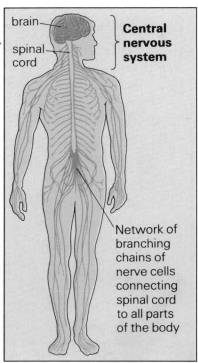

Central nervous system

Network of branching chains of nerve cells connecting spinal cord to all parts of the body

When you touch a hot plate impulses are sent from your fingertips to your central nervous system.

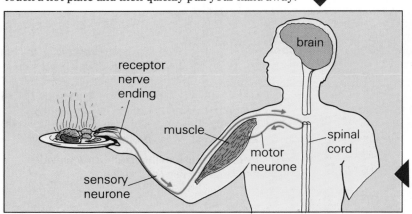

stimulus	receptor	coordinator	effector	response
heat on fingertip	temperature receptors in the skin of the fingertips	spinal cord	muscles in the hand and arm	rapid withdrawal of hand and arm

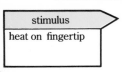 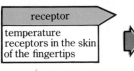 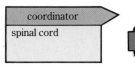

sensory nerves   *motor nerves*

Protecting the body from damage

Pulling your hand away from a hot plate is a **reflex action** – a rapid automatic response to a stimulus which protects the body from possible harm. *Blinking,* when dust gets into your eye; *narrowing the pupil* of your eye in bright light; *coughing* when food goes down the 'wrong way' and touches the windpipe – these are all instant reflexes. In each case you cannot help yourself from reacting – stimulation of particular receptors has caused an *involuntary response* to take place.

The sequence of events in a reflex action, though complex, takes place in an instant. ▼

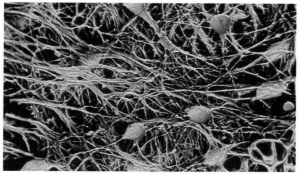

Your brain has millions of nerve cells. Magnified about 200 times, here are some of your brain's 'blob'-like nerve cells. They interact by sending electrical pulses around the brain, controlling all your thoughts and actions.

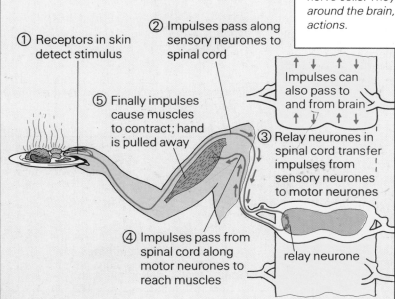

① Receptors in skin detect stimulus

② Impulses pass along sensory neurones to spinal cord

Impulses can also pass to and from brain

③ Relay neurones in spinal cord transfer impulses from sensory neurones to motor neurones

⑤ Finally impulses cause muscles to contract; hand is pulled away

④ Impulses pass from spinal cord along motor neurones to reach muscles

relay neurone

Making decisions

Nerve cells in the spinal cord also carry impulses to your brain to keep it informed about events affecting your body. The brain stores some of this information as **memory.** Unlike reflex actions, many of your other actions are *voluntary* – they are controlled by the brain. For example, after touching a hot plate you may decide to put on a kitchen glove before picking up the plate again. This is possible because you have **learned** from past experience that the plate burns and stored the information in your brain. You can then decide how to act on this information.

---

1 Copy and complete the following table.

Reflex	Stimulus	Receptor	Response	Purpose
Blinking	?	Retina	Eyelid muscles contract	?
Narrowing pupil	Bright light	?	Iris closes	To reduce light entering eye, improves vision
?	Dim light	?	Iris opens	?
Withdrawal of foot	Standing on a sharp nail	?	?	?

2 Use the sequence –

stimulus→receptor→coordinator→effector→response

to explain what happens when:

a you prick your finger with a needle.
b you smell tasty food.

c you accidentally pick up a hot plate and realize it is very expensive!

3.21 Animal reproduction

Sexual reproduction

During sexual reproduction male gametes fuse with female gametes to form **zygotes**. In both animals and plants, the *male* gametes are very small and can move. In contrast, the *female* gametes are fixed in one place and are larger than the male gametes. The male gametes in a plant move down the pollen tube to reach the ovule (*see 3.26*). The male gametes of an animal are the **sperm cells** or **sperm**; the female gametes are **egg cells** or **ova**. When released into a fluid, sperm can swim to reach and fertilise egg cells. Gametes in animals and plants have to be brought close together before the male gamete can move itself towards the female gamete. In plants, **pollination** brings pollen grains (containing the male gametes) close to the ovule (with its female gamete). In animals **mating** brings sperm cells (the male gametes) close to egg cells (the female gametes).

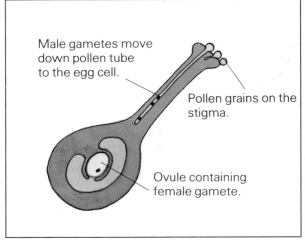

Male gametes move down pollen tube to the egg cell.

Pollen grains on the stigma.

Ovule containing female gamete.

In plants the male gamete moves down the pollen tube to the female gamete.

Animals breeding in water

Many animals live and breed in water. The eggs of these animals, such as fish, toads and frogs, are fertilised *outside* the body of the parent-animal. First the female sheds her eggs into the water. Then the male immediately releases sperm over them – the sperm swim to the eggs and fertilise them in the water. This is **external fertilisation**. The eggs are usually left unprotected and many eggs and young get eaten by predators. Only a small number of species of animals that live in water protect their eggs while they are developing.

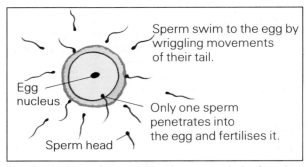

Sperm swim to the egg by wriggling movements of their tail.

Egg nucleus

Only one sperm penetrates into the egg and fertilises it.

Sperm head

In animals the male gamete swims to reach the female gamete.

*As they are laid, the eggs of a frog are surrounded by a jelly-like substance – albumen – which is much the same stuff as surrounds the yolk of a hen's eggs (the 'white' of the egg). This jelly provides some protection for the eggs and causes them to stick together to form **frog spawn**.*

Animals breeding on land

External fertilisation is not possible on land because eggs and sperm would soon dry up. The eggs of animals which live on land are fertilised *inside* the body of the female. This is **internal fertilisation**. Reptiles, birds and mammals place sperm inside the body of the female during mating. The sperm then swim through the moist lining of the female organs to the eggs and fertilise them. In mammals, the fertilised eggs develop inside the body of the female. In contrast the eggs of reptiles and birds are laid outside the body – the hard shell formed around these types of fertilised eggs prevents them from drying up after they are laid. They continue to develop inside the shell until they are ready to hatch into young.

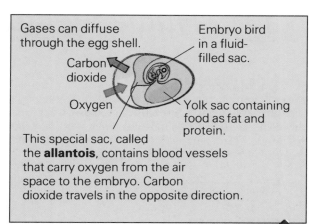

Gases can diffuse through the egg shell.

Carbon dioxide

Oxygen

Embryo bird in a fluid-filled sac.

Yolk sac containing food as fat and protein.

This special sac, called the **allantois**, contains blood vessels that carry oxygen from the air space to the embryo. Carbon dioxide travels in the opposite direction.

The fertilised eggs of birds develop in a hard shell outside the female's body.

Parental care

The eggs of many reptiles, such as turtles, are laid and then also left to develop on their own inside their shells. Birds lay their eggs in a nest and **incubate** them by sitting on them to keep the temperature warm. Most newly-born birds and mammals are protected, fed and kept warm by the parents. The chicks of birds which nest on the ground, such as partridges, are covered with downy feathers at birth and can run around soon after hatching. Chicks of tree-nesting birds, such as blackbirds, hatch with few feathers, closed eyes and limited powers of movement – it takes a few weeks before they can begin to look after themselves.

A blackbird feeding her young. The chicks open their mouths and the bird pushes food down their throats. In a few weeks the young birds are able to fly short distances and find their own food. Soon they can fly away for good.

Eggs for survival

Animals whose eggs have only a small chance of developing into adults need to produce large numbers of eggs to ensure that the species survives. Animals which produce fewer eggs usually provide some parental care of the developing eggs. The table opposite shows the relationship between the number of eggs and the methods of reproduction and development.

Animal	No. of eggs (average)	Development of eggs	Length of parental care (average)
Cod	7 million	in water	none
Stickleback	300	in water	2 weeks
Turtle	15–25	shelled eggs	none
Partridge	8–16	shelled eggs	3 weeks
Blackbird	3–6	shelled eggs	3 weeks
Cat	4	egg develops inside mother	5 weeks

1 Suggest reasons for the following:
   a the trout produces more eggs than the turtle;
   b the trout produces more eggs than the stickleback;
   c the turtle produces more eggs than the blackbird.

2 Predict which eggs in the table will have **a)** the largest store of food, and **b)** the smallest store of food. Explain your answers.

3 Suggest a hypothesis to explain why blackbirds lay fewer eggs than partridges.

4 Female birds lay eggs containing a developing embryo and food surrounded by a hard shell.
   a Name two substances which can pass through the shell. Why must they do so?
   b Why is the fat in yolk a good food to store in a closed egg?
   c Why do the eggs of frogs and trout not need a hard shell?

Human reproduction

Producing gametes

Sexual reproduction in humans also involves the production of gametes, like any other animal. **Sperm** are produced by the man in tiny tubes inside his **testes**. **Eggs** (or **ova**) are produced by the woman in her **ovaries**. The diagrams show the tissues involved in the production and release of gametes in humans. ▼

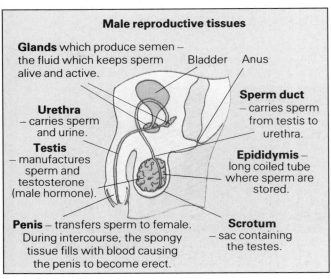

Male reproductive tissues

Glands which produce semen – the fluid which keeps sperm alive and active.

Bladder   Anus

Urethra – carries sperm and urine.

Sperm duct – carries sperm from testis to urethra.

Testis – manufactures sperm and testosterone (male hormone).

Epididymis – long coiled tube where sperm are stored.

Penis – transfers sperm to female. During intercourse, the spongy tissue fills with blood causing the penis to become erect.

Scrotum – sac containing the testes.

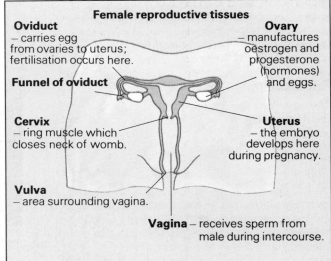

Female reproductive tissues

Oviduct – carries egg from ovaries to uterus; fertilisation occurs here.

Ovary – manufactures oestrogen and progesterone (hormones) and eggs.

Funnel of oviduct

Cervix – ring muscle which closes neck of womb.

Uterus – the embryo develops here during pregnancy.

Vulva – area surrounding vagina.

Vagina – receives sperm from male during intercourse.

Action of hormones

The testes and ovaries of humans do not produce gametes until **puberty** is reached – usually around the age of 11–14 years. Your sex organs mature at this age because the **pituitary gland**, a small gland near your brain, releases the hormones **FSH** and **LH** into your bloodstream. These hormones are released continuously after puberty, and act on the testes and ovaries.

In *boys*, they stimulate the testes to produce sperm and to release the male sex hormone **testosterone**. This hormone controls the development of male characteristics such as growth of the penis, testes and body hair. In *girls*, the release of FSH and LH controls the production of eggs and the release of the female sex hormones, **oestrogen** and **progesterone**, by the ovaries.

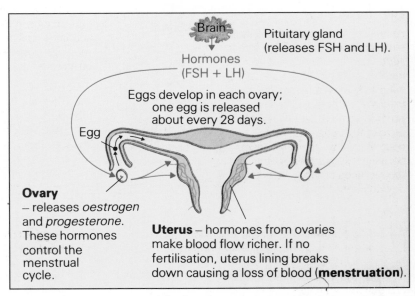

Brain

Pituitary gland (releases FSH and LH).

Hormones (FSH + LH)

Eggs develop in each ovary; one egg is released about every 28 days.

Egg

Ovary – releases *oestrogen* and *progesterone*. These hormones control the menstrual cycle.

Uterus – hormones from ovaries make blood flow richer. If no fertilisation, uterus lining breaks down causing a loss of blood (**menstruation**).

The pituitary hormones and the female sex hormones begin to control changes in a young woman's ovaries and in her uterus in her early teens. This is marked by the onset of menstruation (monthly period).

The start of life

Usually just one mature egg is released from one or other ovary during **ovulation** – once every 28 days or so. It then passes along the oviduct towards the uterus, a journey which takes about 7 days. If the egg meets a sperm within 1 to 3 days after being released, it can be **fertilised**. If it is not fertilised, it will break up as it passes along the oviduct. Sperm will only be present in the oviduct if sexual intercourse has recently taken place. **Semen** (a mixture of sperm and nutritive fluid) is **ejaculated** from the penis into the vagina at the climax of intercourse. Once inside the vagina, the sperm swim through the cervix and along the uterus towards the oviduct. Millions of sperm are released into the vagina at ejaculation, but only a few of the healthiest ones will reach the oviduct. The fusion of a sperm and an egg is called **fertilisation** (or **conception**). The cell that is formed, the **zygote**, continues to pass along the oviduct towards the uterus. As it passes along, the single-celled zygote divides several times, so that by the time it reaches the uterus, it is like a ball of cells. This ball of cells, called an **embryo**, sinks into the lining of the woman's uterus – a process called **implantation** – and the woman is now pregnant.

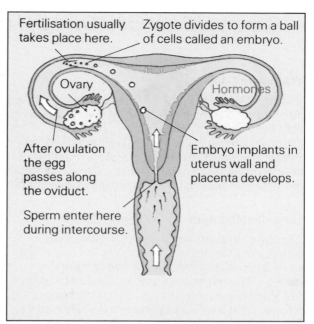

Fertilisation or conception takes place when a sperm, released during intercourse, fuses with an egg inside the oviduct of the woman.

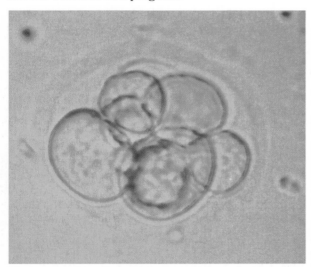

There are eight cells in this human embryo. Can you see them all? Starting from a single fertilised zygote, how many divisions have occurred to reach this stage?

Technology assisting nature

Some women have blocked oviducts. In the past women with this problem could not have children. A technique has been developed which overcomes this. The technique (often called making 'test-tube' babies) involves fertilising a human egg *outside* the body. This is known as **in vitro fertilisation**. Injections of FSH and LH are given to the woman so that she produces a mature egg. A doctor makes an incision in the abdomen wall and inserts a fine tube through it to suck the eggs from her ovary. (The hormone treatment often causes many eggs to be released at the same time.)

The eggs are placed into a solution containing a mixture of food, salts, oxygen and water. Semen (from the father) is then mixed with the eggs to fertilise them. The fertilised eggs are kept in the solution to develop into embryos for a few days. Then an embryo is implanted by the doctor into the mother's uterus.

[1] Explain how changes take place in the development of boys and girls when FSH and LH are released from the pituitary gland.

[2] Why do women usually release only one egg a month when many fish release millions?

[3] Use the diagrams to list, in the correct order, **a** the male tissues that sperm pass along after being made in the testes, and **b** the female tissues that sperm pass along after being released in the vagina.

[4] **a** Explain why a blocked oviduct prevents fertilisation.
   b How are eggs and sperm kept alive outside the body during 'in vitro' fertilisation?
   c Explain why doctors inject FSH and LH before attempting to remove mature eggs.

3.23 *Development in the womb*

Warm, well-fed and protected

Your life, like every human life, started from a zygote the size of a full stop! It takes 38 weeks for this single cell to develop into the millions of cells that make up a newborn baby. This period of important rapid growth and development, called the **gestation period**, takes place inside the mother's womb or **uterus**. It is a characteristic of all mammals. By developing inside the mother's body, the young mammal is kept warm, is fed by the mother, and is protected from damage and from predators.

Early development

The human zygote initially divides several times as it passes along the oviduct, to form a ball of cells called an **embryo** which sinks into the soft lining of the uterus. This embryo then receives food and oxygen from the blood flowing through the uterus lining of the woman. After 3 weeks, a **placenta** develops (on the lining of the uterus) from some of the cells of the embryo. The **umbilical cord** connects the developing embryo to the placenta and acts as a lifeline, bringing food and oxygen to the foetus from the mother's placenta and taking away excretory substances. After only 4 weeks in the uterus, the embryo is 46 mm long and has a beating heart! You can recognise certain human features after 8 weeks – from around this stage the embryo is known as a **foetus**. Women usually begin to feel the foetus kicking after it is about 16 weeks old. From 27/28 weeks onwards the foetus has a good chance of surviving an early – **premature** – birth, provided it is given special hospital care.

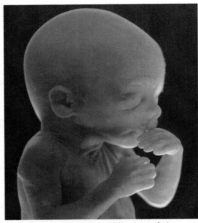

A 20-week-old foetus. All the organs and limbs of the developing baby are well formed at this stage.

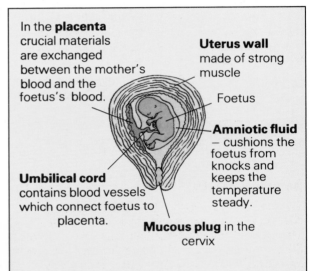

In the **placenta** crucial materials are exchanged between the mother's blood and the foetus's blood.

Uterus wall made of strong muscle

Foetus

Amniotic fluid – cushions the foetus from knocks and keeps the temperature steady.

Umbilical cord contains blood vessels which connect foetus to placenta.

Mucous plug in the cervix

The foetus develops while being fed and protected inside the mother's womb.

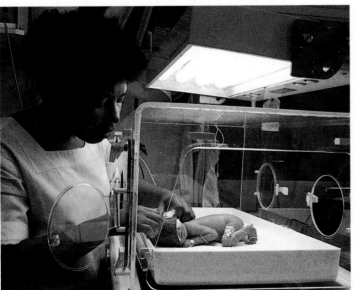

In or out – which is the best? A very premature baby can survive in an incubator which supplies the main provisions of the mother's womb – warmth, food and oxygen.

The placenta

The placenta is essential for the growth of a healthy baby. The functions of the placenta are:

- To absorb **oxygen** and **food** substances such as glucose and amino acids from the mother's blood.
- To release the hormones **oestrogen** and **progesterone** which are needed to prevent the shedding of the uterine lining.
- To excrete waste substances such as **carbon dioxide** and **urea** into the mother's blood.

The placenta is an extremely efficient organ for exchanging substances. Like other organs for exchange, such as the lungs and the small intestine, it has a *large surface area*, it is *thin*, and it has a very *good blood supply*.

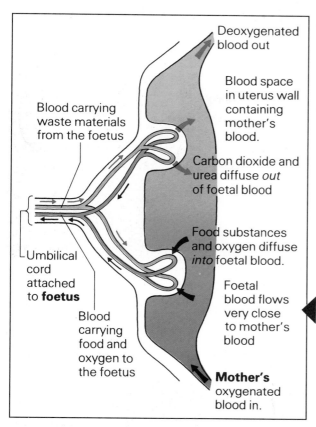

Deoxygenated blood out

Blood space in uterus wall containing mother's blood.

Blood carrying waste materials from the foetus

Carbon dioxide and urea diffuse *out* of foetal blood

Food substances and oxygen diffuse *into* foetal blood.

Umbilical cord attached to **foetus**

Blood carrying food and oxygen to the foetus

Foetal blood flows very close to mother's blood

Mother's oxygenated blood in.

Harmful substances

Oxygen and food are not the only substances that can pass across the mother's placenta to the foetus. Women who *smoke* have **carbon monoxide** and **nicotine** in their blood. If a woman smokes during pregnancy these substances will pass to the foetus. Carbon monoxide restricts the oxygen supply to the foetus. Nicotine puts stress on the foetal heart by making it beat more quickly. **Alcohol** can also damage the foetus. Women who *drink alcohol* during pregnancy run the risk of having smaller and underdeveloped babies. Many other kinds of **drugs** can be harmful to the foetus if they are taken during pregnancy. In the 1960s, many pregnant women took a drug called thalidomide to help them sleep better and to relieve tension during their pregnancies. The drug caused many babies to be born with severely deformed limbs.

The placenta is an essential organ for exchanging materials so that the foetus continues to survive all through the gestation period.

This table shows one effect that smoking during pregnancy may have on newborn babies. ▼

		Number of babies born to non-smoking mothers	Number of babies born to smoking mothers
Mass at birth (Kg)	Less than 2.4	4	3
	2.4 to 3.1	42	24
	3.2 to 3.5	70	44
	3.6 to 3.9	54	23
	Greater than 3.9	30	6
	Total in sample	200	100

Harmful organsims

The placenta also protects the developing foetus from disease. A bacterium or virus that causes a disease in a mother can only reach the foetus by passing across the placenta. The **rubella virus** that causes German measles is one that can. This virus can seriously damage a foetus which is infected in the first 3 months of its development. This is why *all* young women should be vaccinated against rubella *before* they are able to become pregnant. The **AIDS virus** can also be passed on by a woman to her baby. The life expectancy of a baby born with AIDS is only a few months.

1 Use the table of birth mass above to answer the following questions.
  a What percentage of babies had a birth mass greater than 3.5 kg in
    i non-smoking mothers?
    ii smoking mothers?
  b Use the data to give one effect of smoking on birth mass.
  c Suggest a possible reason for this effect.

2 **a** Name three substances that will be more concentrated in the foetal blood flowing *into* the placenta than blood flowing *out*.
  b Explain how the structure of the placenta is suited to its job of exchanging substances between the foetus and mother.

3 Explain why babies born to heroin and crack addicts can suffer withdrawal symptoms after birth.

The newborn baby

A new life

Birth usually takes place in the 38th week of pregnancy. A few weeks before birth, the foetus usually comes to lie in the **birth position** – with its head nearest the woman's cervix. The woman's body begins to release certain hormones which start the birth process by bringing about regular **contractions** of the muscles in her uterus wall. This is when she goes into 'labour'.

Being born is quite an amazing experience! The first nine months of your life as a foetus are spent in the very stable, dark and fluid environment of your mother's uterus. Suddenly at birth, you are exposed to very different conditions! When inside the mother, feeding, gaseous exchange and excretion are carried out for the foetus by the placenta. After being born a baby has to start maintaining its own life – and all those complex functions!

An umbilical cord – it connects the baby to the mother's placenta in the womb. After the birth the baby begins to breathe, feed and excrete on its own. So the cord is cut – leaving us all with a belly button!

Maintaining early life

The first breath a baby takes is a **reflex action** (*see 3.20*) stimulated by the sudden fall in temperature outside the mother's body. The air entering the baby's lungs causes them to inflate for the first time and gaseous exchange begins to take place. Unlike many other animals, humans are quite helpless when they are first born. Their parents have to do a lot for them. Like all mammals, humans **suckle** (provide milk for) their young. During the first 3 to 4 months milk (breast or bottle) provides all a baby's energy needs and nutrients, except for iron. Babies obtain the iron they need to make haemoglobin from their mother during pregnancy and store it. Many mothers choose to breast-feed their babies because human milk is perfect for a baby's dietary needs. It is also produced at the right temperature, at low cost and is even hygienically packed! Breast milk also contains **antibodies** from the mother – special substances which protect the body from disease.

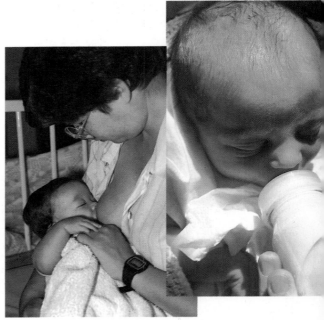

Is breast best? If you had a baby what would you prefer to do – breast feed it or bottle feed it? Think of all the pros and cons for both.

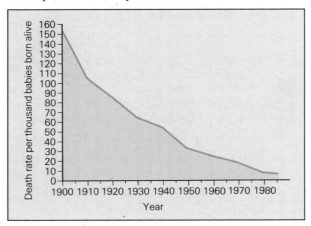

Infant mortality

The graph opposite shows how many babies (out of every thousand born) died in their first year since 1900. As you can see, there has been a very big fall in the **infant mortality rate**, but even so about 10 babies in every thousand still die before their first birthday.

▌ Why do you think the mortality rate for young babies has decreased so rapidly?

Fighting childhood diseases

Many babies used to die from infectious diseases caused by bacteria or viruses. Now deaths from serious diseases such as whooping cough, polio and diphtheria are much less common in this country – because babies are **immunised** against them. Once children are immune to a particular disease, they will not catch it.

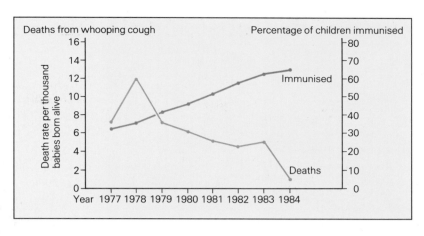

The graph shows the effects of immunising children against whooping cough in recent years. Do you think the programme has been effective?

This child has chicken pox. It is a fairly harmless disease but very infectious. Once you have had it you will be immune in the future.

Age	Immunisation given
3–6 months	1 Diptheria, whooping cough, tetanus, polio
4–6 weeks later	2 Diphtheria, whooping cough, tetanus, polio
4–6 weeks later	3 Diphtheria, whooping cough, tetanus, polio
1–2 years	Measles
4–5 years	Diphtheria, tetanus, polio
10–13 years	BCG vaccination against TB if skin test negative
11–14 years	Rubella (German measles) – girls only
15 years	Tetanus and polio

Natural immunity to disease

There are many diseases which you will only catch once. This is because you develop a **natural immunity** to the disease. For example, when the virus that causes chicken pox enters your body, it grows and gives the symptoms of chicken pox. You recover from the disease because your white blood cells produce antibodies that destroy the virus. The next time the virus enters your body, you will already have the right antibodies present in your blood. A *different* type of antibody is needed to fight off *each type* of virus or bacterium.

Providing immunity

Babies and young children can be protected from many of the more serious diseases by 'persuading' their bodies to make the necessary antibodies. When you are immunised against a disease, a *harmless* form of the virus is introduced into your body deliberately. This makes your body produce antibodies that also make you immune to the *harmful* form of the virus. To protect infants and children from disease, all infants in the UK begin an **immunisation programme** when they are about three months old – this should continue until they are about 15 yrs.

Keeping your child up to date with vaccinations is an important part of your responsibility as a parent. Doctors keep records and issue reminders to help you keep a check.

1. In the early 1970s some parents became concerned about the safety of the whooping cough vaccine – they considered the side effects of the vaccine were quite risky. Some decided not to have their babies immunised. What effect did this have?

2. The World Health Organisation (WHO) try to persuade mothers in developing countries to feed their babies on breast milk rather than powdered milk. What are the advantages of breast milk for these mothers and babies?

3. Suggest reasons why infant mortality has declined so rapidly since 1900.

3.25 *Being responsible about sex*

Sometimes science textbooks can give the impression that sexual intercourse is all about reproduction. But humans are different! For many people having sex is an important part of a loving and caring relationship.

As you grow older some of your relationships with other people begin to change.

Forming relationships

As people mature they may find that some of their relationships with others change. Young people often experience intense curiosity about sexual matters and sexual attraction can be a factor in some of their relationships.

Having sex does not have to be part of a loving relationship; and if young people do decide to have sex they need to be responsible about it.

Taking responsibility

Which of these ideas do you most agree with? What do *you* think is meant by 'being responsible' about sex? Some people might say that to be responsible is simply to ensure that you don't risk unwanted pregnancies or sexually transmitted diseases. Many others feel that to have sex when your body is mature but possibly not your emotions is something that you may be sorry about later. There are many things to learn and enjoy about the other person as you begin a loving relationship and you shouldn't feel pressurised into having sex. Why do you think that it's illegal in the UK to have sex under the age of sixteen?

Preventing conception

For many people preventing conception is important as they may want to have a specific number of children at a time convenient to them. For people such as these it's important to choose a contraceptive method that is *not* permanent.

1   The condom or sheath

Condoms work by preventing ejaculated sperm entering a woman's vagina. They are made from very thin rubber and are unfurled onto the erect penis before sex begins. They are very reliable, cheap and easy to buy. They also have the extra benefit of protecting against sexually transmitted diseases.

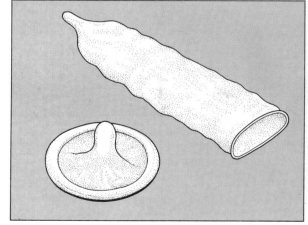

A condom.

2 The diaphragm or cap

A diaphragm is made of soft rubber in the shape of a shallow cup. It has a flexible metal ring. The diaphragm is filled with spermicidal cream and inserted to fit over the cervix. This prevents sperm from entering the uterus. Like condoms, diaphragms are reliable and have no side effects. They must be fitted for individual women by a nurse or doctor.

3 The contraceptive pill

The contraceptive pill interrupts the menstrual cycle by introducing synthetic versions of female hormones. The level of hormones in the pill makes the woman's body 'think' she is pregnant and so she does not ovulate.

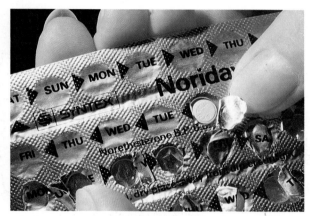

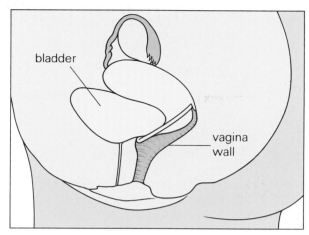

A diaphragm fitted over the cervix.

Sexually transmitted diseases

Sexually transmitted diseases (STDs) are, obviously, those which are passed on through sexual intercourse. Some people find this fact alone frightening and so they are inhibited about admitting to being infected. Many STDs are curable and it is essential for anyone who thinks they are infected to visit their G.P. Initial signs of infection are often minor but must be treated immediately to avoid serious problems later.

Herpes, syphilis and gonorrhoea

The **herpes** virus causes blisters rather like cold sores on or inside the penis or vagina. Herpes is passed to sex partners when the virus is active. It is not curable and can cause infection of babies during birth. The **syphilis** bacteria at first causes painless sores on the sex organs which later vanish. At this stage syphilis can be treated effectively with antibiotics. Later in life untreated syphilis can lead to blindness, paralysis and death. **Gonorrhoea** is another bacteria which if untreated can lead to sterility. Males experience a discharge from the penis and pain when urinating. 70% of women experience no early symptoms which makes the disease very dangerous.

AIDS

AIDS is caused by the HIV virus which can be transmitted sexually as well as through blood contact. The high risk groups are:
- men and women who have many sexual partners
- drug users who share needles
- haemophiliacs who have been given infected blood

AIDs cannot be transmitted by holding hands.

Protection and prevention

It is absolutely essential to protect yourself from STDs as some – like AIDS – are incurable. You are increasing your risk if you have many sex partners but the diseases are actively transmitted during *one* encounter. So to be safe it's best not to have many sex partners and if you do have sex to *use a condom*.

Producing new offspring

Plants and animals cannot live for ever. Each type of organism needs to produce more of its own kind by the process of **reproduction**. This process may be asexual or sexual.

Many organisms – some plants and simple animals – reproduce on their own *without another individual*. We call this **asexual reproduction**. For example, cells from plant roots, stems or leaves may grow to produce new plants. (This is also called vegetative reproduction.)

Sexual reproduction involves *two* individuals and requires the production of special sex cells called **gametes** (made in the reproductive organs of the plant or animal). During the process of **fertilisation**, the male gamete fuses with the female gamete to form a single cell called a **zygote**, which then grows into a new individual.

Mosses reproduce asexually by producing spores inside a spore capsule. When ripe the capsule bursts and the spores are scattered forming more individuals.

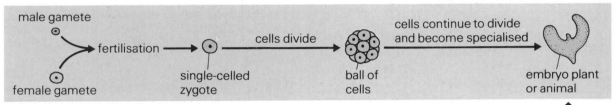

Sexual reproduction occurs in plants as well as animals. It always involves the fusion of gametes to form a zygote.

Sexual reproduction in plants

Flowers contain the reproductive organs of the plant. Their job is to produce gametes – and to bring male and female gametes close together, so that fertilisation can take place. The *male* gamete is in the **pollen grain** produced in the **anther** of a flower. The *female* gamete is in the **ovule** which lies in the **ovary**. Attached to the ovary are the **stigma** and **style**. Before fertilisation can occur, pollen from the anthers has to be *transferred* to the stigma. This process is called **pollination**. The transfer of pollen from the anther of one flower to the stigma of another flower of the same type is called **cross-pollination**. Pollen grains can be carried on the bodies of insects (insect pollination) or blown around in the wind (wind pollination).

> Using the diagram, identify the features of the insect-pollinated flower which increase its chances of being pollinated.

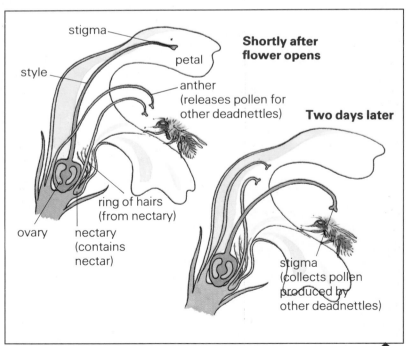

Flowering plants such as this white deadnettle are cross-pollinated by insects. Just how do you think the pollen gets from one flower to another?

A bee feeding on the nectar of one flower gets covered in pollen. When it visits another flower (to feed again!) some of the pollen from the first plant will get onto the stigma (of the second plant), thereby pollinating the second plant.

The wind will transfer the pollen from the anthers of this common alder flower to the stigma of others for cross-pollination.

Nature's way

Different plants are constructed to help pollination occur easily. *Wind*-pollinated flowers often hang down so that they are easily shaken. *Insect*-pollinated plants often have beautiful colours and scents (and supplies of sugary nectar) to attract the insects into the plant's waiting reproductive organ – the flower!

Producing seeds

Pollination is complete when pollen (from a first plant) has landed on a stigma (of a second plant) and the process of fertilisation begins. The cells of the stigma produce a sugary fluid which nourishes the pollen grains – this helps them to grow to form a **pollen tube**. The diagram shows how the pollen tube then grows towards the female gamete in the ovary. The pollen tube contains the male gamete (from the *first* plant) which fuses with the female gamete (in the *second* plant) to form a zygote. The zygote is a single cell which grows to form an **embryo** plant. The fertilised ovule grows to form a **seed**. Each seed has a hard outer coat to protect it and also contains a store of food surrounding the embryo plant.

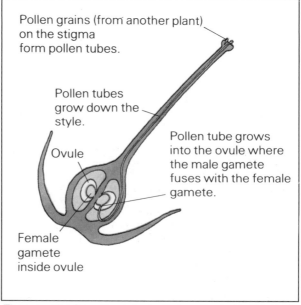

Pollen grains (from another plant) on the stigma form pollen tubes.

Pollen tubes grow down the style.

Ovule

Pollen tube grows into the ovule where the male gamete fuses with the female gamete.

Female gamete inside ovule

The growth of a pollen tube to the ovule carries the male gamete to the female gamete.

1 **a** Make a copy of and complete this table to compare wind- and insect-pollinated flowers.

	Insect	Wind
Stigma	Sticky to take pollen from insects	?
Petals	?	Small with little or no colour
Nectar and scent	?	?

b Suggest reasons for each of the differences given in the table.

2 **a** State *two* changes that you can observe in the white deadnettle opposite that take place in the two days after opening.
  b Explain how these changes help to make sure that these flowers are cross-pollinated.

3 A scientist observed that some types of flowers produce small amounts of pollen grains with spiky surfaces. Other types of flowers produce very large quantities of smooth and light pollen grains.

What do these observations tell you about how these flowers are pollinated? Explain your reasoning.

3.27   *Plant seeds and germination*

Embryo plants

At **fertilisation** in plants, the male gamete from a pollen grain fuses with (fertilises) a female gamete to form a **zygote** (*see 3.26*). Hormones in the ovules are then released by the plants which stimulate the development of **seeds** from fetilised ovules. Each seed contains an **embryo** plant which grows from the zygote. A store of food is also formed in the seed to provide the embryo plant with the energy and chemicals it will need to survive and grow. Seeds, such as peas and beans, are a popular source of food for us. You'll come across other seeds inside fruits you eat – the pips in apples and oranges, for example. The **fruit** is the part of a plant which surrounds the seed or seeds.

Many seeds survive through bad conditions – freezing winters, drought and so on – by going into a **dormant** stage. Respiration and other chemical processes slow down to a very low level during dormancy – the seed appears to be dead, but will begin to grow in suitable conditions.

You can eat a whole variety of tasty seeds – these will contribute nutrients and vitamins to your balanced diet.

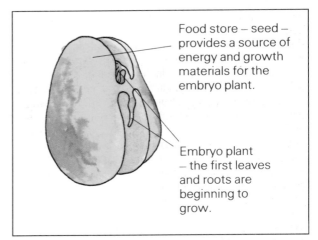

Food store – seed – provides a source of energy and growth materials for the embryo plant.

Embryo plant – the first leaves and roots are beginning to grow.

A seed contains an embryo plant and a source of food for it to use to grow.

Scattering seeds

When seeds fall from the parent plant they are scattered over a wide area. This avoids overcrowding and competition for light and water – for the right conditions in which to grow.

It also enables plants to spread into – **colonise** – new habitats. Seeds and fruits containing seeds can be dispersed by wind, animals and by 'explosive' pods. The diagrams below show how the structure of some common seeds is adapted to suit various methods of dispersal.

Study the diagrams carefully. How does the structure of each seed or fruit ensure that it is dispersed over a wide area?

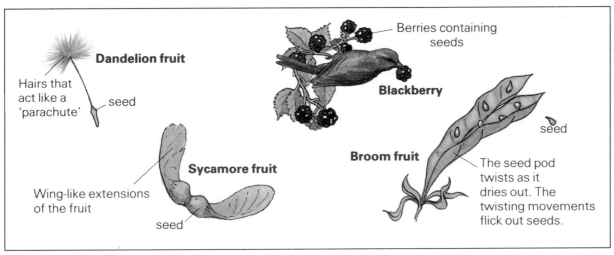

Dandelion fruit

Hairs that act like a 'parachute'

seed

Sycamore fruit

Wing-like extensions of the fruit

seed

Berries containing seeds

Blackberry

Broom fruit

seed

The seed pod twists as it dries out. The twisting movements flick out seeds.

Germination of seeds

Seeds which land in suitable places – where there is water and light – will begin to grow into young plants. This process is called **germination**. A number of changes take place inside the seed as germination begins. *Water* is absorbed by the seed. This makes the seed swell and softens the seed-coat so that it eventually splits. *Enzymes* in the seed become active – and break down the insoluble stored food into soluble foods (such as sugars) that can be transported to the growing embryo. Sugars are used, along with oxygen (from the air or soil), in **respiration** by the embryo to provide energy for growth. The embryo forms young roots that grow out through the split seed-coat and into the soil to keep the plant in place, absorbing water and nutrients. The young shoot grows upwards, develops leaves, and begins to **photosynthesise**. For all these changes to take place, the germinating seed needs a supply of **water** to transport food and enzymes, **oxygen** for respiration, **light** for photosynthesis, and a suitable **temperature** for enzyme activity.

From seed to shoot: (Top left) A dried-out pea seed before germination; below, a germinating pea which has soaked up water for a day. One day later, the seed coat is set to burst (bottom right). Finally the shoot and root emerge – one up, one down.

Plants without seeds

Seeds are formed as a result of sexual reproduction. New plants can also be formed by **asexual reproduction**. Strawberry 'runners' and the 'eyes' on potato tubers are products of asexual methods of forming new plants (*see 3.26*). If you take a cutting from a plant you are making a new plant artificially by using asexual reproduction. When you plant the cut end of a stem in compost or soil, roots *may* develop from the cut stem. Some cuttings will fail to form roots and so die.

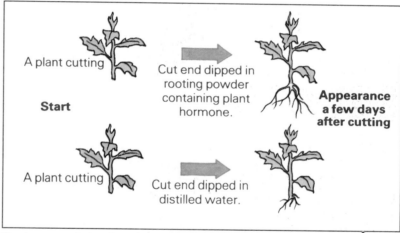

A plant cutting
Start
Cut end dipped in rooting powder containing plant hormone.
Appearance a few days after cutting

A plant cutting
Cut end dipped in distilled water.

Gardeners and plant breeders use rooting powder containing plant hormones to increase the success rate of making new plants from cuttings.

1. Describe how the seeds of the following plants are dispersed:
   Dandelion
   Strawberry
   Peas

2. **a** Look at the diagram above. Give one difference between the two sets of cuttings two days after planting.
   b How does treatment with hormone powder help the cuttings to grow?

3. Some seeds were collected from the droppings of a bird which had fed on some berries. Another set of seeds was collected from berries that had fallen from the tree.

Both sets of seeds were placed in moist soil and put in a warm place. After four days the number of seeds that had germinated was counted.

	Percentage germination
Seeds from bird droppings	85
Seeds from fallen berries	40

a Suggest two hypotheses to explain how seeds are affected as they pass through the bird's gut.
b Describe a method of testing each hypothesis.

YOU CAN READ MORE ABOUT RESPIRATION AND PHOTOSYNTHESIS ON SPREADS 2.1, 2.4.

4.1 *Molecules that make life*

You're unique

There may be many people in your school but you can easily be recognised from the rest. In fact, there are over 5 000 million people on the Earth and each one is different. These differences are called **variations**. Your hair colour, eye colour, weight and height are just a few of the **characteristics** that vary – and distinguish you from everyone else.

Family likeness

It is often easy to tell that related people are members of the same family because they have similar characteristics. The similarity between children and parents suggests that some characteristics are *inherited* – passed on from one generation to the next. Investigating family trees is one method that is used to study human **inheritance**.

A family tree showing that some members have red hair and some are talented musicians.

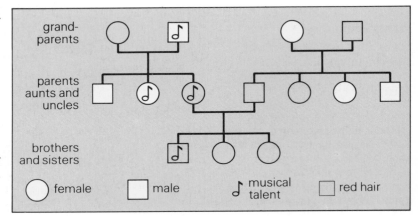

grand-parents				
parents aunts and uncles				
brothers and sisters				
◯ female	☐ male	♩ musical talent	☐ red hair	

Working on your inheritance

Not all characteristics are simply passed on from parents. For example, the strength and ability to become an Olympic athlete are not just inherited – they depend on the right lifestyle, diet and training as well as natural talent. In other words, physical strength and ability are affected by **environmental factors**. Many other human characteristics, such as height and weight, are influenced by environmental as well inherited factors.

You need more than natural talent to reach the top.

What will I become?

What will this baby be – a football star? prime minister? rock guitarist? This will depend on many things but some aspects of the baby's future will have been determined already. Inside each of the millions of cells that make up the baby's body is a chemical called **DNA** (deoxyribonucleic acid) which contains instructions to make an entire human being. DNA is an extremely long spiral molecule divided into regions called **genes**, which provide *coded* instructions for particular characteristics, such as hair colour. Many human features are affected by the DNA that we inherit – intelligence, state of health and even life span.

The human code

If the DNA from every cell in your body was unravelled and joined end to end, it would stretch to the Moon and back about 8 000 times! This huge amount of DNA contains millions of individual genes. Techniques have been developed that enable scientists to isolate and analyse the coded instructions in single genes. In 1989, scientists from all over the world became involved in a project to identify every gene in the human body – and reveal the complete human code. At present, only a fraction of the total DNA instructions have been analysed, and it will be many years before this DNA testing works out the complete instructions for making a human being.

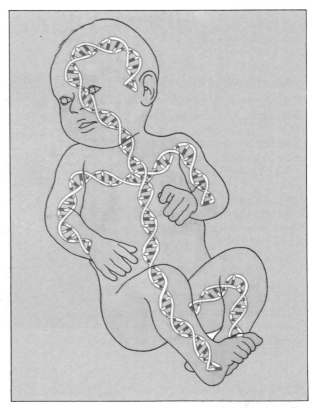

DNA contains the complete code to make an entire human being.

Changing inheritance

DNA testing has helped to identify some faulty genes which cause serious illnesses. It might be possible to treat people with such illnesses using **gene therapy** – replacing faulty genes with normal ones. The new techniques for analysing DNA are also probing the mystery of how disorders such as cancer and heart disease develop.

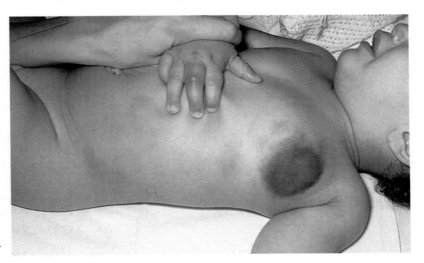

Even a small knock can result in large bruises in this child because he suffers from haemophilia (excessive bleeding) – a disease caused by a faulty gene. ▶

1 When a group of students examined the data in the family tree on the opposite page, they produced the hypothesis that 'red hair and musical talent are inherited characteristics'.

State, giving your reasons, whether you agree or disagree with their hypothesis.

2 Do you think being good at science is an inherited characteristic? Give reasons for your answer.

3 DNA testing will present us with many difficult problems, for example:
- should someone who will develop a deadly disease later in life be told?
- should gene therapy be used only for treating diseases or also for improving other inherited features?

a What other possible problems can you think of?

b Do these problems mean that we should stop this form of testing?

4.2 Human variation

Similarities and differences

People, like most other living organisms, vary in many ways. The family shown here have features in common but each member differs from the rest. The children have similar features to their parents because of the common genes they inherit. For example, they may inherit genes which produce curly hair and genes which may make them tall. Even though brothers and sisters have similar features, no two children (except identical twins) will inherit *exactly* the same genes. We each inherit a *different* mixture of genes from our parents, making each of us different from everyone else.

Members of the same family inherit similar features.

Measuring variation

A survey of variation was carried out on 200 first-year pupils in a high school. Two characteristics were measured – pupils' height and their ability to roll their tongue into a U-shape. The results of the survey are shown in these histograms.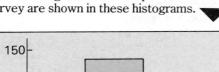

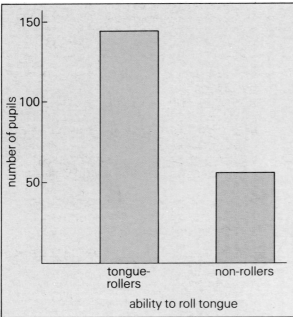

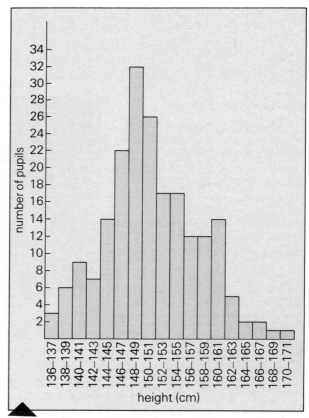

In this histogram there is a *continuous* range of height from the tallest pupils to the smallest. This type of variation is called **continuous variation**.

There are no half-way values for tongue rolling – people either can roll their tongue or they cannot. This type of variation is called **discontinuous variation**.

Effects of the environment

A girl may inherit genes that could make her tall, but if she is undernourished, she will not grow to her full height. All characteristics which show *continuous* variation are *affected by the environment* as well as by inherited factors.

Tongue-rolling is just one example of discontinuous variation. Another example is your blood group. People belong to one of four main blood groups A, B, AB or O. Like all examples of *discontinuous* variation, your blood group is *entirely due to your genes* and is not affected by your environment.

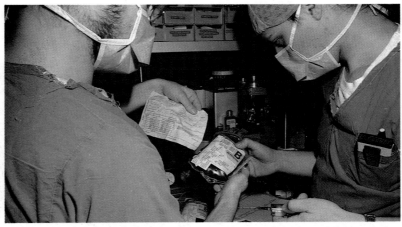

People can become very ill if they are given blood of the wrong group during transfusion. ▲

Investigating variation

Identical twins develop from the same fertilised egg cell. This means that they are born with *identical* genes which control their future growth and development. Investigations involving identical twins can provide valuable information about how characteristics are affected by inherited and environmental factors.

Katie and Rebecca are identical twins who were separated at birth and brought up in different families. When they were 16 years old, the following data was recorded about them:

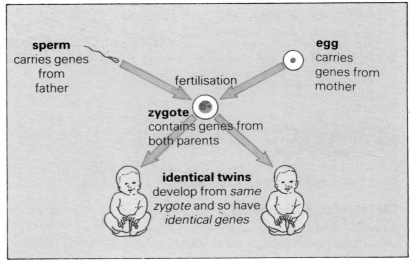

sperm carries genes from father

egg carries genes from mother

fertilisation

zygote contains genes from both parents

identical twins develop from *same zygote* and so have *identical genes*

	Katie	Rebecca
weight	62 kg	51 kg
hair colour	red	red
freckles	present	present
measure of intelligence	134	119

1 Use the evidence in the table about the twins to suggest, with reasons
  a which characteristics are controlled by inherited factors only,
  b which are influenced by the environment in which the girls were raised,
  c which characteristics show continuous variation.

2 Look at the survey of pupils' height on the opposite page.
  a What number of pupils were 160 cm or taller?
  b Give *two* reasons why the pupils show a large variation in height.
  c Name one other human characteristic which shows the same type of variation.

3 In another investigation into variation, the maximum span of the right hand was measured. The results were:

hand span (mm)	number of students
170–179	2
180–189	5
190–199	9
200–209	6
210–219	3

  a Draw a histogram of these results.
  b What type of variation is shown by hand span?

97

4.3 Passing on information

Like mother, like daughter

'Doesn't she have her mother's eyes?' 'Isn't she like her father?' are typical of the comments that friends and relatives make when they first see a young girl. How are these features inherited?

The diagram below shows the main events that take place during **fertilisation**. What does this diagram tell you about how genetic information can be passed from parent to offspring?

When the nuclei of a sperm and egg join together, the first cell of a new individual is formed – the zygote. ▼

Many of this baby's characteristics have already been determined.

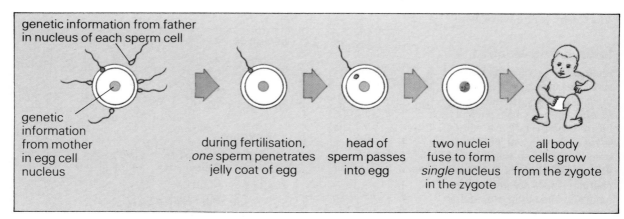

genetic information from father in nucleus of each sperm cell

genetic information from mother in egg cell nucleus

during fertilisation, *one* sperm penetrates jelly coat of egg

head of sperm passes into egg

two nuclei fuse to form *single* nucleus in the zygote

all body cells grow from the zygote

The material of inheritance

A new life starts when the nucleus from a sperm *fuses* with the nucleus of an egg at fertilisation to form a single-celled **zygote**. The material that is present in the nuclei of the sperm and egg is the *only* material that passes from parents to their offspring. The sperm and egg contain information which affects how we grow and what we look like. This is called **genetic information**.

When a cell is not dividing, the nucleus appears as a dark region inside the cell. During cell division, thread-like **chromosomes** can be seen in the nucleus. Each chromosome contains enough genetic information to control thousands of characteristics. The chromosomes in eggs and sperm carry genetic information from the mother and father to their offspring.

Through a microscope, you can see thread-like chromosomes when cells divide. ▼

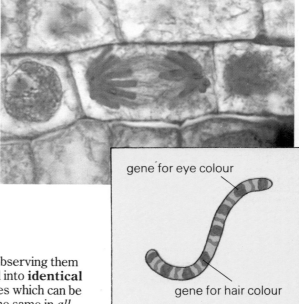

gene for eye colour

gene for hair colour

Each gene in a chromosome ▲
controls a particular characteristic.

Pairing up

Chromosomes appear in different shapes and sizes. By observing them very carefully, the chromosomes in a cell can be grouped into **identical pairs**. For example, human cells contain 46 chromosomes which can be grouped into 23 pairs. This number of chromosomes is the same in *all* body cells – you have 23 pairs of chromosomes in each of your skin cells, eye cells, bone cells and so on.

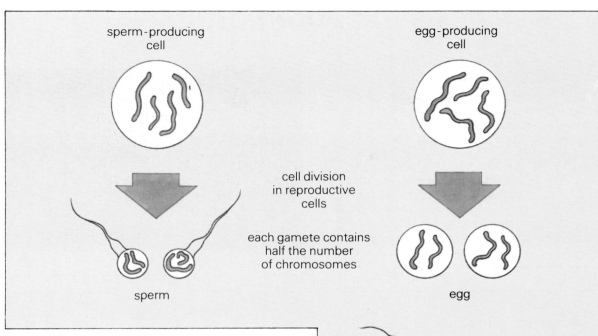

sperm-producing
cell

egg-producing
cell

cell division
in reproductive
cells

each gamete contains
half the number
of chromosomes

sperm

egg

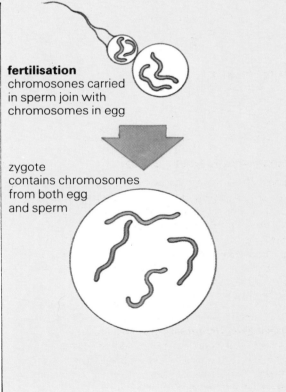

fertilisation
chromosones carried
in sperm join with
chromosomes in egg

zygote
contains chromosomes
from both egg
and sperm

Halving the number of chromosomes . . .

Chromosomes are passed from parents to their offspring by reproductive cells called **gametes**. Gametes are produced by a special form of **cell division** that takes place in reproductive organs. During this process, the pairs of identical chromosomes separate from each other and move into different cells. The gametes formed by this cell division contain only *half* the number of chromosomes in normal body cells. For example, each sperm or egg cell contains 23 chromosomes.

. . . and restoring the number of chromosomes

The first cell of a new individual is formed when gametes fuse at fertilisation. Each gamete carries a single set of chromosomes, so the zygote that is formed by their fusion contains *both* sets. For example, when a human sperm carrying 23 chromosomes fuses with a human egg carrying 23 chromosomes, a zygote is formed with 46 chromosomes. The chromosomes in the zygote are again found as identical pairs. Each pair has one chromosome from the male gamete and one from the female gamete.

1. The number of chromosomes found in the cells of a particular species is always the same. Human cells contain 46 chromosomes while the cells of cats have 38. How many chromosomes will be found in
   a a cat skin cell?
   b a cat sperm cell?
   c a cat muscle cell?
   d a cat zygote cell?

2. The diagram below shows the chromosomes in the root cell of a plant.

Draw diagrams to show the chromosomes in
   a a leaf cell,
   b a pollen grain, of the same plant.

YOU CAN READ MORE ABOUT REPRODUCTION ON SPREADS 3.22 AND 3.23.

4.4 *Looking at chromosomes*

The start of life

Your life started from a single cell called a zygote, produced at fertilisation. This contained all the genetic information needed to make you. The information that determined whether you became a boy or a girl, tall or short, blue-eyed or dark-eyed, was present in the chromosomes in the zygote. All your body cells developed from this single cell by **simple cell division**. During this process, *all* the genetic information is copied into new cells so that all the cells in your body contain an *exact* copy of the chromosomes that were present in the zygote.

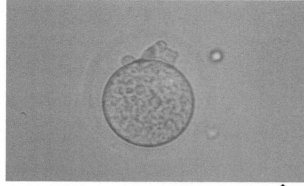

When you were 'one' you had just begun . . . you started life as a single zygote like the one above.

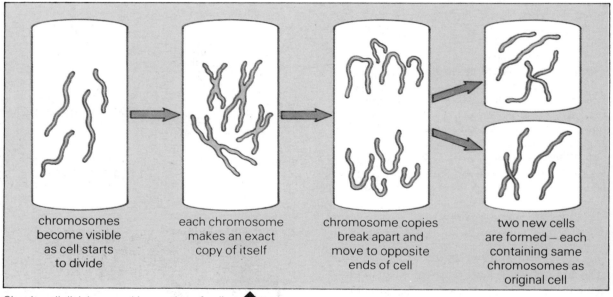

| chromosomes become visible as cell starts to divide | each chromosome makes an exact copy of itself | chromosome copies break apart and move to opposite ends of cell | two new cells are formed — each containing same chromosomes as original cell |

Simple cell division – making copies of cells.

Checking development

Some women are given a special test during their pregnancy to check that the foetus is developing normally. During this test, called **amniocentesis**, a small amount of fluid is removed from around the foetus. The fluid contains chemicals and cells from the foetus which doctors can examine to check foetal development. For example, doctors can identify several abnormalities that may occur in the foetus by examining the chromosomes in the cells. They can also see whether the foetus is going to be a boy or a girl.

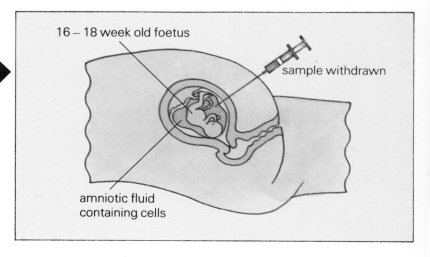

16 – 18 week old foetus

sample withdrawn

amniotic fluid containing cells

Boy or girl?

These diagrams show the appearance of some chromosomes from two healthy foetuses. Only 6 out of the 23 pairs of chromosomes are shown in each case. By looking at these chromosomes, doctors identified one foetus as male and the other as female. Can you identify any difference between the two sets of chromosomes?

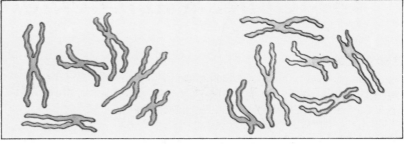

How do the chromosomes in the male differ from those in the female?

Sex chromosomes

Whether you became a boy or a girl was determined by one pair of chromosomes in the cells of your body – the **sex chromosomes**. In females, the sex chromosomes are identical to each other and are called **X chromosomes**. In males there are two types of sex chromosome: one is the same as the female sex chromosomes, an X chromosome, while the other is shorter and is known as the **Y chromosome**. So in females the sex chromosomes are XX and in males they are XY. As you can see from this diagram, sex is determined by the sex chromosome of the sperm that fertilises the egg.

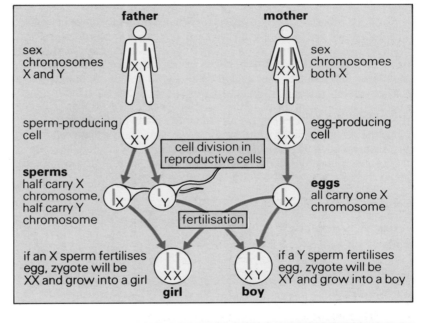

Checking for abnormalities

Examining the cells obtained by amniocentesis enables doctors to check for a disorder called **Down's syndrome**. Children with this disorder will have some mental retardation and may also have heart and respiratory (breathing) problems. The disorder is caused by a **mutation** – a change in the genetic material of an organism. Children with Down's syndrome have an extra chromosome in their cells, giving them 47 instead of the usual 46 chromosomes.

Many children with Down's syndrome lead happy lives, despite the disorder.

1 Draw a large, clear copy of the diagram of the chromosomes of the male foetus shown at the top of this page.
   a Draw a ⬚box⬚ around any two identical chromosomes,
   b draw a ⟨circle⟩ around the X chromosome, and
   c underline the Y chromosome.

2 The male foetus will eventually grow into an adult. Draw diagrams to show the appearance of chromosomes in this foetus's
   a cheek cells,
   b possible types of sperm cells.

3 a What are the chances that the first baby in a family will be a boy? Explain why.
   b What are the chances of the next baby being a boy?

4.5 Genes and inheritance

The odd one out

Sandy kept a pair of pet brown rabbits and was pleased to find they were breeding. But when he looked at the litter, he was puzzled – three of the young rabbits had shiny brown fur like their parents, while one was completely different with white fur. What could have caused this unexpected variation?

Gene control

The cells of complex organisms contain thousands of **genes**. Each gene controls a *particular* inherited characteristic, such as fur colour in rabbits. The genes that are present in an organism are called its **genotype**. Each gene forms part of a chromosome. Since chromosomes occur in identical pairs, each cell contains a *pair* of genes for each characteristic. The cells of rabbits, for example, contain two genes for fur colour. Although the two genes determine the same characteristic they may have different effects. The different forms of the same gene are called **alleles**. One of the genes (alleles) that controls fur colour in rabbits produces brown fur while the other produces white fur. The way genes are shown in an organism is called its **phenotype**. You can see in this diagram how the different combinations of the genes for fur colour present (the genotype) affect the fur colour of rabbits (the phenotype). ▼

Notice that a rabbit only has white fur when both genes for white fur are present.

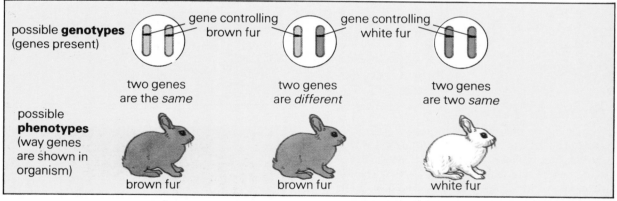

Dominant and recessive

When the gene for brown fur and the gene for white fur are both present, the rabbit is brown. This is because the gene for brown fur *masks* the other gene. The gene for brown fur is a **dominant** gene and the gene for white fur is **recessive**. A dominant gene is usually indicated by a capital letter and a recessive gene by a lower-case letter.

Explaining inheritance

The idea that some genes are dominant while others are recessive was put forward by **geneticists** – scientists who study genes and inheritance. Geneticists *observe* **patterns of inheritance** and try to *explain* them. They do this using a knowledge of what happens to chromosomes and genes during reproduction.

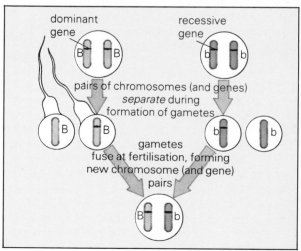

The two main events that occur during reproduction.

Tracing the path of chromosomes

How would geneticists explain the white rabbit? As a first step, they would make a **hypothesis** about the genotypes of the parent rabbits. Then they would trace the movement of chromosomes in reproduction to find out what genotypes the offspring are likely to have.

Follow the movement of chromosomes shown below, based on this hypothesis:

Hypothesis: both parent rabbits contain a dominant *and* recessive gene for fur colour, so both can pass on a recessive gene to their offspring.

Do you think the hypothesis is correct?

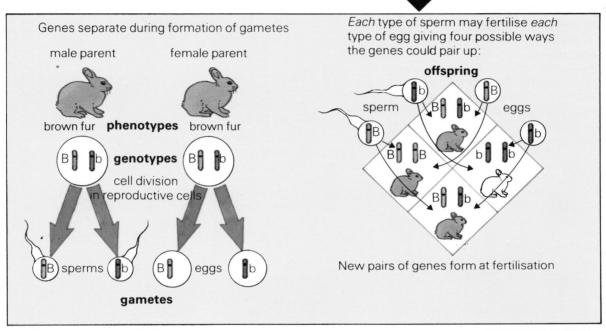

Predicting patterns of inheritance

You can use the knowledge of what happens to genes and chromosomes to *predict* the genotypes and phenotypes of offspring. This diagram shows a cross between a brown rabbit and a white rabbit. Study it carefully and then answer the question below.

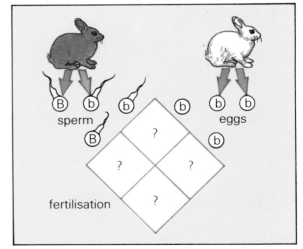

1
  a Make a copy of and complete the table of gamete fusion.
  b Predict the ratio of brown : white rabbits in the next generation.

2 Suppose Sandy's rabbits had two white young and two brown young. Would this mean that the hypothesis at the top of this page is correct? Explain your answer.

3 Flower colour in pea plants is controlled by a pair of genes. The gene for white flower colour is recessive (r) and the gene for red colour is dominant (R). When a heterozygous plant with red flowers was pollinated by a plant with white flowers, 40 new plants were produced.

  a What hypothesis would you make about the genotypes of the parent plants?
  b How many of the new plants would you expect to be white?
  c The number of white flowered plants obtained was actually 13. Does this mean that your hypothesis in **a** is incorrect?

Unusual phenotypes

This diagram shows inheritance of coat colour in a breed of cattle called Shorthorns. There are two genes, R and W, that can control coat colour in Shorthorns. Both Genes (RR) in the red bull control red hair colour and both genes (WW) in the white cow control white hair colour. The calves inherit one gene from each parent and so have the genotype RW. You might expect the calves' coat colour to be red *or* white. Instead, *all* the calves have *both* white and red hairs giving them a pale red or roan coat colour. How does this phenotype come about?

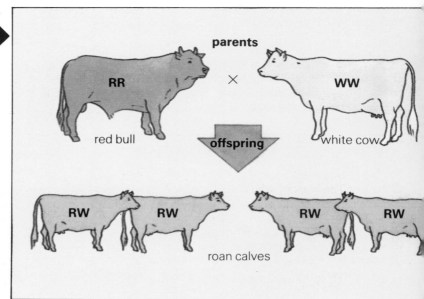

Co-dominant genes

Since the calves have red *and* white hairs, *both* the genes (R *and* W) must be showing their effect in the phenotype – neither of the genes dominates the other. This is called **co-dominance**.

Expected ratio of red : roan: white calves = ?

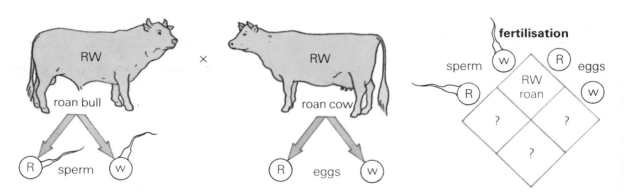

What happens if you cross a roan cow and a roan bull? Study this diagram carefully, and then copy and complete the table to show the possible results of gamete fusion. Use your table to predict the ratio of the phenotypes of the calves that will be produced from the cross.

Predicting blood groups

Your blood group may be controlled by co-dominant genes. There are four blood groups A, B, AB and O. These groups are controlled by three genes A, B, and O. Gene O is recessive to genes A and B. When both genes A and B are present, they show co-dominance. Since genes occur in pairs, only two of the genes are present in any one person.

Copy and complete this table.
Sam's father is blood group AB and his mother is blood group O. Which blood groups could Sam be? How did you arrive at your answer?

blood group		possible genotypes
	A	AA or AO
	?	BB or ?
	?	AB
	O	?

Your blood group is controlled by genes.

Colour blindness

Some people cannot distinguish between the colours red, brown and green. This is a type of colour blindness which can be tested for using charts like the one shown here. People who are colour blind can experience difficulties in many situations – for example, noting colour changes in chemicals during science lessons, or cheering the 'right' team!

Not everyone can see the number in the dots. ▶

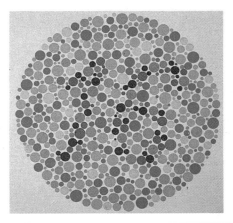

▌This shows part of the family tree of Tim Walker, who is colour blind. Examine the pattern of inheritance carefully. Do you think that the gene that causes colour blindness is dominant or recessive? ▶

Sex-linked inheritance

One of Tim's grandfathers is colour blind, then the condition misses a generation and re-appears in Tim. This suggests that colour blindness is caused by a *recessive* gene. You can also see that both colour blind members of the Walker family are *male*. In fact, far more males than females are colour blind. This is because the gene for colour vision is carried on the X chromosome and is *absent* from the Y chromosome.

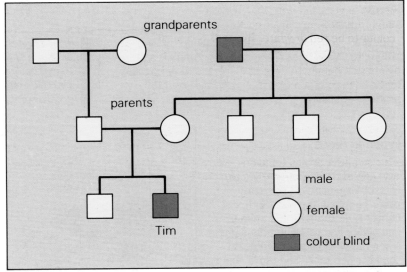

1 **a** Give some examples from everyday life when Tim Walker may experience problems because of his colour blindness.
 b From which parent, his mother or father, do you think Tim inherited the gene for colour blindness?
 c If Tim marries a girl whose family have *no* history of colour blindness, what are the chances that any son they may have will be colour blind? Explain your answer.

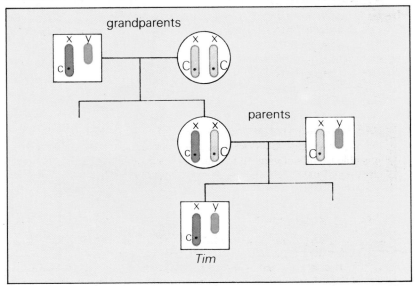

2 Mr Khan is blood group O and Mrs Khan is blood group A. One of their daughters is blood group O like her father.
 a Use this information to work out the genotype of Mrs Khan.
 b What are the chances of Mr and Mrs Khan having a child with blood group A? Explain how you arrived at your answer.

*Colour blindness is called a **sex-linked condition** because the gene is carried on a sex chromosome.* ▲

4.7 Forming new species

Sorting living things

There is a huge variety of living things in the world. The millions of organisms have some features in common but they also differ from each other in many ways. These similarities and differences can be used to arrange organisms into groups – a process called **classification**. For example, nearly all living things can be classified as either animals or plants. The animals shown here are placed into a smaller group using their *similar* features. Their *different* features can be used to divide this group into even smaller groups.

The smallest group that scientists use is called a **species** – you and all the other people in the world belong to the species *Homo sapiens*. Animals and plants that belong to the same species have so many features in common that they can *interbreed* to produce offspring.

These water animals are all classified as arthropods because of their similar *features*, such as exoskeletons and jointed limbs. *What* differences *do you think could be used to separate them into smaller groups?*

Evolving ideas

The Swede, Carolus Linnaeus, was one of the first scientists to classify organisms. Like many other people in the sixteenth century, he thought that animals and plants had remained the same since the world was created. As they learned more and more about plants and animals, some scientists began to question the theory that species had always been the same. Instead they suggested that species *change* and that *new* species are being formed all the time. This is the **theory of evolution** which proposes that all species evolved from a common ancestor by a process of *gradual change*. Many scientists accepted this theory but Charles Darwin was the first to collect evidence and put forward an explanation of how evolution takes place.

Scientists believe that all mammals – including you – evolved from a small shrew-like creature through gradual change over millions of years.

Gathering evidence

In 1831, the young Darwin was offered a place as a naturalist on the survey ship *HMS Beagle*. The five-year voyage took Darwin all round the world, and he was amazed by the tremendous variety of animals and plants he found. After returning to Britain, he spent the next 20 years studying and trying to explain the origins of his enormous collection of animals, plants and fossils. Eventually he put forward the theory that evolution might have occurred through **natural selection**.

Struggling to survive

Darwin's theory of natural selection is based on the four ideas shown here. ▼

1. Organisms produce many offspring.

2. Organisms struggle to survive.

3. Members of a species vary.

4. Characteristics that give an organism an advantage are more likely to be passed on to the next generation.

The Galapagos finches

During the *Beagle's* voyage, Darwin became fascinated by the animals and plants found on the small Galapagos Islands in the Pacific Ocean off the coast of South America. He noticed that the species on these islands were similar to species found on the South American mainland – but many of the Galapagos species differed from their mainland relatives in small ways. For example, there are 13 species of Galapagos finches that are found nowhere else in the world. Some islands even possess particular species of finches that are not found on the other islands. To explain these observations, Darwin suggested that a few finches had strayed to the islands from the mainland. As they bred in their *different* and *isolated* environments, the finches gradually changed or evolved into new species.

There are no woodpeckers on the Galapagos Islands so these woodpecker finches have adapted to feed on the insects in tree crevices.

1 The main groups used in the classification of living things are:
phylum species class kingdom genus.

Place these groups in order of their size, starting with the largest. You may need to use reference books to do this.

2 In the struggle to survive, some organisms are killed by predators while others survive. What other factors affect the survival of organisms?

3 Darwin realised that variation is necessary for natural selection to occur. He searched for an explanation of variation but was unsuccessful. Using your knowledge of genetics, try to explain the causes of variation.

4 Why was *isolation* on separate islands an important factor in the evolution of the Galapagos finches?

4.8 Selection in action

Testing the theory

According to the theory of natural selection, the characteristics of a population slowly change as individuals become *better adapted* to their environment. Darwin gave examples of populations that he thought had changed through adaptation. Since then, many investigations have been carried out which show natural selection in action.

Changing with the times

A good example of natural selection is shown by a species called the peppered moth. There are two varieties of this moth – a pale and dark variety. The first dark moth was found near Manchester in 1848. At that time the dark variety was rare, but since then it has become very common in *industrial* areas. Scientists believe that this change in numbers of the dark variety is the result of natural selection.

Peppered moths feed at night and rest on tree trunks and branches during the day. In areas with little or no industry, tree trunks are encrusted with lichens giving them a mottled grey appearance. In industrial areas, pollution in the air kills the lichens and blackens the trees. The dark variety of moth has an advantage in this environment because it is better camouflaged against the dark trees. So the dark variety is more likely to *survive* and *produce offspring* in industrial areas than the pale variety.

The pale and dark varieties of peppered moth . . . ▼

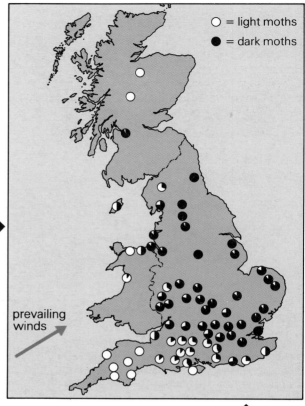

The proportion of dark and light varieties of ▲ peppered moth found in different areas of Britain today.

*. . . in each picture, which of the **two** moths will survive?*

Super rats

If you had rats in your house, they would gnaw through any stores of food. As well as being pests, rats are also a serious health hazard – by contaminating food with harmful bacteria they can spread diseases to people. So wherever rats are found, poison is put down. Warfarin started to be used as a rat poison in the 1950s. By 1980, many areas in Britain had populations of warfarin-resistant rats. These 'super' rats failed to die even when they ate large doses of warfarin. Many pest species develop a **resistance** to the pesticides used on them.

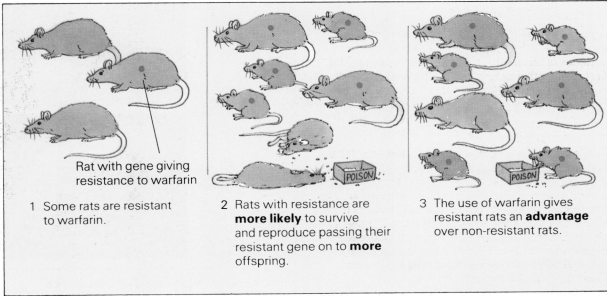

Rat with gene giving resistance to warfarin

1 Some rats are resistant to warfarin.

2 Rats with resistance are **more likely** to survive and reproduce passing their resistant gene on to **more** offspring.

3 The use of warfarin gives resistant rats an **advantage** over non-resistant rats.

 How resistance to warfarin spreads in a population of rats.

The three possible genotypes and phenotypes for resistance in rats.

Genotype	Phenotype
WW	warfarin resistant but needs large amounts of vitamin K
Ww	warfarin resistant and needs only small extra amounts of vitamin K
ww	killed easily by warfarin

Genes controlling resistance

Warfarin kills rats by stopping their blood from clotting. Resistance to warfarin is controlled by a *dominant* gene, W (*see 4.5*). Recent studies have shown that rats which have two dominant genes (WW) require very large amounts of vitamin K – a vitamin which is also needed for blood to clot. It these rats fail to get enough vitamin K they bleed to death.

1 Study the distribution map and photographs of the peppered moth on the opposite page and then answer these questions
  a In which areas are pale moths more common?
  b How does being well camouflaged aid survival?
  c Why is the *pale* variety more common in some areas than others?
  d What would happen to the peppered moth population if the industry in north-west England changed and the amount of pollution in the air decreased? Explain your answer.

2 **a** Which genotype gives the best advantage to rats? Explain why.
  b If two rats with this genotype bred, what genotypes could the offspring have? Predict the ratio of these genotypes.
  c Will the recessive gene that causes rats to be killed by warfarin ever be totally wiped out? Explain your answer.

Tailor-made plants and animals

'Improving' nature

People have grown crops and kept domesticated animals for thousands of years. Until recently, no one knew how inheritance worked, but it was obvious that characteristics were passed from parents to offspring. So people *controlled* the breeding of plants and animals to develop the characteristics they wanted, such as faster growth, higher yields and more resistance to disease. They selected and bred from plants and animals with the desired characteristics. The process is called **artificial selection** and has resulted in many new varieties of animals and plants.

More milk from cows

Farmers have increased milk production through careful breeding programmes, using only the bulls and cows with the most suitable characteristics. These programmes have gradually developed **breeds** of cattle with much higher milk yields than their ancestors. The breeding programmes have been helped enormously by **artificial insemination** – taking semen (fluid containing sperm) directly from the male and inserting it into the female. Using artificial insemination, a single bull can pass on desirable characteristics to many offspring without actually mating. By freezing semen, it is even possible for a bull to continue to sire offspring after its death. However, as this table shows, not all animals are suitable for use in artificial insemination programmes.

Why is artificial insemination ▼
particularly useful for cattle?

Modern varieties of crops, such as this high-yielding wheat with lots of 'ears', have helped to increase our food supplies. ▼

Many years of careful breeding have increased the meat yield of domestic pigs – and made them very different from their ancestor, the wild boar. What differences can you see? ▼

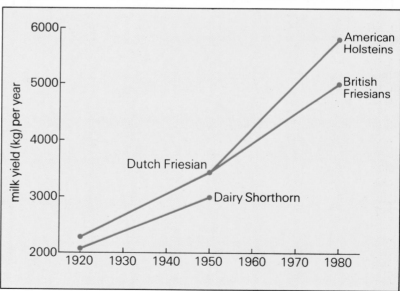

This graph shows the increase in ▲
milk yields of some breeds of cattle,
produced by artificial selection.

Farm animal	Volume of semen obtainable from a single sample (cm³)	Easily frozen	Number of inseminations from a single sample
horse	50–100	no	90
cattle	5	yes	500
sheep	1	no	25
pig	200–250	no	35

Speeding up breeding

Only the 'best' cows (those with the required characteristics) are selected for breeding. The number of offspring that could be produced from selected cows used to be limited by the long **gestation period** – the time it takes for the embryo calf to develop. This problem can now be overcome by extracting eggs from the best cows and fertilising them outside the body (**invitro fertilisation**). Alternatively, the eggs can be fertilised inside the mother and the fertilised eggs or **zygotes** extracted.

Multiplying and checking offspring

A short time after fertilisation, the zygote has divided many times, forming a ball of *identical* cells. Each cell of this developing young or **embryo** can be separated and grown into a new embryo, using a technique called **tissue culture**. This enables a large number of embryos *with identical genes* to be produced from a single embryo. The individuals that develop from these embryos will be identical – they will be **clones**. Each embryo is then transplanted into an 'inferior' cow. Before transplantation, each embryo's DNA may be tested for inherited diseases. In 1990, scientists identified the gene that determines the sex of an individual. So in the future, breeders may be able to control the sex of calves. This is very important if you are a dairy farmer and want only cows.

Modern technology has given animal breeders far more control.

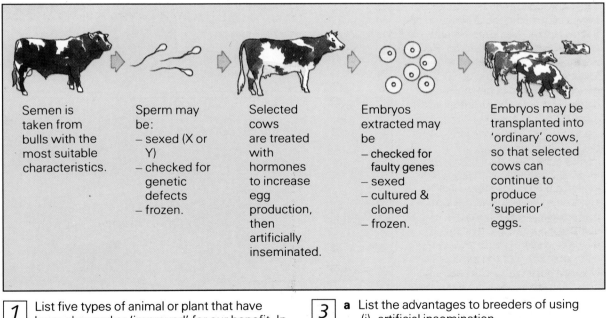

| Semen is taken from bulls with the most suitable characteristics. | Sperm may be:
 – sexed (X or Y)
 – checked for genetic defects
 – frozen. | Selected cows are treated with hormones to increase egg production, then artificially inseminated. | Embryos extracted may be
 – checked for faulty genes
 – sexed
 – cultured & cloned
 – frozen. | Embryos may be transplanted into 'ordinary' cows, so that selected cows can continue to produce 'superior' eggs. |

1 List five types of animal or plant that have been changed or 'improved' for our benefit. In each case, state their use to us.

2 Look at the graph opposite.
 a Why did milk production increase rapidly in 1950?
 b Explain why milk production continued to increase after this year.

3 a List the advantages to breeders of using
   (i) artificial insemination.
   (ii) embryo transplants.
 b Do you think such techniques should be used on farm animals? Discuss this question in a group.

YOU CAN READ MORE ABOUT IN VITRO FERTILISATION ON SPREAD 3.22

4.10 *Sickle-cell disease*

Blood disease . . .

Your blood transports vital materials, such as food and oxygen, around your body. The oxygen is carried by a substance called **haemoglobin**, contained in red blood cells. These cells are usually disc-shaped. In 1910 doctors found that a large number of children in west Africa were suffering from a very severe form of **anaemia** – a disease in which the blood fails to carry sufficient oxygen. The red blood cells of these children were sickle-shaped and so the disease was named **sickle-cell anaemia**. People with the disease died early in childhood.

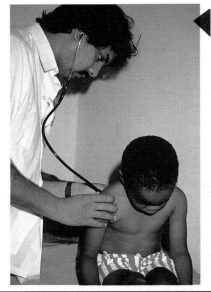

This child has sickle-cell anaemia – a painful deadly disease caused by a faulty gene.

. . . caused by genes

Shortly after discovering the disease, doctors found that the parents of children with sickle-cell anaemia had a very *mild* form of anaemia known as **sickle-cell trait**. This caused little, if any, ill effect. Children with sickle-cell anaemia were *only* born into families in which *both* parents had sickle-cell trait. From this evidence, doctors concluded that sickle-cell anaemia is an *inherited* disease and that it is caused by a **co-dominant gene** (*see 4.6*). It is now known to be caused by one of the co-dominant genes controlling the production of haemoglobin. The gene N controls the production of normal haemoglobin, while the gene S leads to the production of *abnormal* haemoglobin which distorts red blood cells into a sickle shape.

Most people's red blood cells look like this . . .

The red blood cells of people with sickle-cell anaemia look like this . . .

People with sickle-cell trait have red blood cells that look like this . .

Most of the cells are disc-shaped, but a few may become sickle-shaped.

A puzzling distribution

Since most people with sickle-cell anaemia died before they had children, doctors expected that few people would inherit the abnormal S gene and that the disease would become less and less common. Yet the number of children born with sickle-cell anaemia remained at the high level *in certain areas*. Then people noticed that the disease was most common in areas of the world where another deadly disease, **malaria**, also occurred. Malaria is caused by a parasite that spends part of its life in red blood cells. But how could malaria affect the distribution of sickle-cell anaemia?

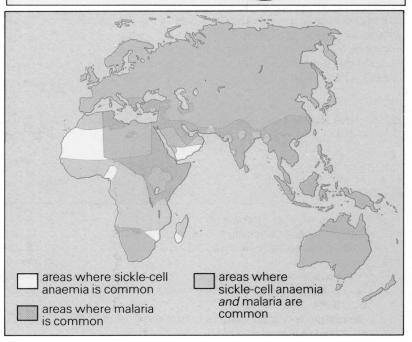

☐ areas where sickle-cell anaemia is common

☐ areas where malaria is common

☐ areas where sickle-cell anaemia *and* malaria are common

YOU CAN READ MORE ABOUT BLOOD AND HAEMOGLOBIN ON SPREAD 3.9.

The link with malaria

Malaria affects the distribution of sickle-cell anaemia because the abnormal S gene provides **resistance** to malaria – people with the S gene are unlikely to die from malaria. This diagram shows the possible combinations of N and S genes (the genotypes) and their effects.

Which genotype do you think would be of most advantage in
- malaria areas?
- non-malaria areas?

Explaining the distribution

The distribution of sickle-cell anaemia can be explained by **natural selection** (*see 4.7*). Many people die of sickle-cell anaemia or malaria before they are old enough to have children. So in areas where *both* diseases occur, N and S genes are *removed* from the population. But N and S genes are also *passed on* in the population because people of genotype NS are most likely to survive. These two effects of natural selection maintain both the N and S genes in populations in malaria areas – and maintain the number of children with sickle-cell anaemia.

Preventing genetic disease

Doctors help couples with sickle-cell trait to consider the risk of having a child with sickle-cell anaemia. After such **genetic counselling** couples may decide not to have children. Doctors can also diagnose many genetic disorders, including sickle-cell anaemia, in the very early stages of pregnancy. This provides couples with the choice of whether to continue the pregnancy. Medical scientists are now developing a technique called **gene replacement therapy**, which will enable them to replace one gene with another – for example, replace S genes with N genes. In the future, this technique may cure sickle-cell anaemia and many other inherited diseases.

1 **a** What evidence is there to show that sickle-cell anaemia is an *inherited* disease?
b Explain why doctors concluded that the disease is caused by a *co-dominant* gene.

2 Why is sickle-cell disease much more common in west Africa than in Britain?

3 Gene replacement therapy may provide a cure for inherited diseases – and allow *other* inherited features to be changed. Many people are worried about this technique.
a Why do you think people are concerned about replacing genes?
b State, with reasons, whether you think research into gene replacement therapy should continue.

Genotype	Effect
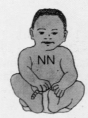	People of genotype NN produce *normal* haemoglobin – and have *little* resistance to malaria.
	People of genotype SS have *abnormal* haemoglobin and suffer from sickle-cell anaemia. They are resistant to malaria.
	People of genotype NS have the very mild sickle-cell trait. They are resistant to malaria.

In areas where malaria is common, people with NS genotype are most likely to survive and have children . . .

. . . and 1 in 4 of their children is likely to suffer from sickle-cell anaemia.

4.11 *Inherited disease*

Faulty genes

The genes present in the cells of your body control all your inherited characteristics. Some people inherit 'faulty' genes and these can cause **inherited diseases**. A faulty gene may result in only a minor defect, such as poor vision, but some cause very serious illness. Faults are produced by mutations (changes in genetic material) which can alter single genes or whole chromosomes. Down's syndrome is the result of **chromosome mutation** (*see 4.4*). Cystic fibrosis and haemophilia (excessive bleeding) are examples of inherited diseases caused by **gene mutation**.

Children with cystic fibrosis need regular physiotherapy to keep their chests clear. ▼

Deadly inheritance

Cystic fibrosis is a very common inherited disease in the UK – about one child in every 2 000 is affected by the illness. Children with the disease produce very thick and sticky mucus. This can block the air passages to the lungs and block the small ducts which carry digestive enzymes to food in the gut. These blockages cause repeated chest infections and poor absorption of food. In the past, no one with cystic fibrosis survived to adult life. Today doctors cannot *prevent* infections but strong antibiotics and vigorous chest physiotherapy do help the child to recover. However, each bout of infection leaves the lungs slightly more damaged so the child becomes gradually more and more ill.

Blood clotting

A serious loss of blood could make you very ill – or kill you. When you cut yourself, the wound in your skin is sealed by a **blood clot**. This stops blood loss and keeps the wound clean. The blood clot forms because **enzymes** (substances that enable chemical reactions to take place in your body) convert a *soluble* blood protein into a fibrous, *insoluble* protein. A blood clot usually only forms when blood vessels are damaged. What would happen if a blood clot formed in a healthy blood vessel?

When your skin is cut, a clot forms. This stops you losing too much blood and prevents germs from entering your body. ▶

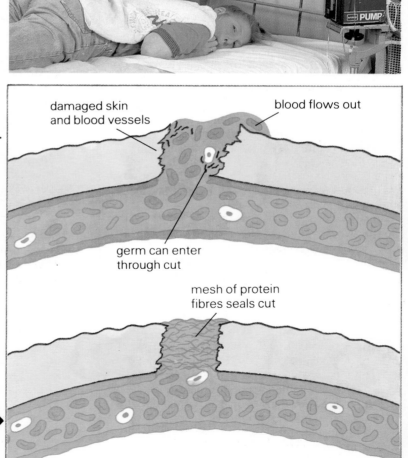

damaged skin and blood vessels

blood flows out

germ can enter through cut

mesh of protein fibres seals cut

Clotting factors

The enzymes that convert soluble blood protein into fibrous protein only work when certain **clotting factors** are present. This diagram shows how one important clotting factor – **factor 8** – works together with enzymes to clot the blood. ▼

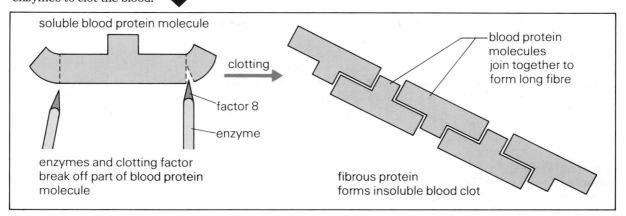

soluble blood protein molecule

clotting

factor 8

enzyme

enzymes and clotting factor
break off part of blood protein
molecule

blood protein
molecules
join together to
form long fibre

fibrous protein
forms insoluble blood clot

Lack of factor 8

Haemophilia is a disease in which the blood fails to clot or clots only very slowly. When a person with the disease is cut or bruised, they may bleed so much that they die. Haemophiliacs bleed excessively because their blood lacks the clotting factor 8. So the enzyme cannot work properly and no blood clot forms. The disease is due to a recessive gene which fails to produce factor 8.

Enzymes cannot work without the clotting factors. ▼

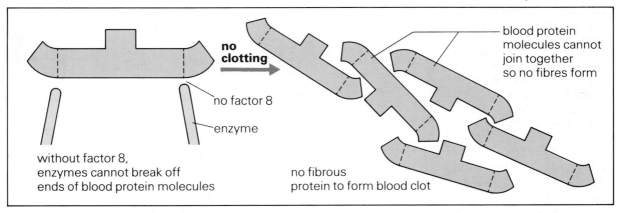

no
clotting

no factor 8

enzyme

without factor 8,
enzymes cannot break off
ends of blood protein molecules

no fibrous
protein to form blood clot

blood protein
molecules cannot
join together
so no fibres form

---

1 Cystic fibrosis is an inherited disease which involves a pair of genes.

Two healthy parents had three children. Two of the children were also healthy but the youngest child suffered from cystic fibrosis.
a Is the gene that causes cystic fibrosis dominant or recessive? Explain your answer.
b What are the genotypes of the parents?
c What is the chance of a fourth child also having the disease? Draw a diagram to show your reasoning.
d Inherited diseases, such as cystic fibrosis, are more common if the parents are cousins than if the parents are unrelated. Explain why.

2 Stephen is a haemophiliac. Neither of his two brothers have the disease. When Stephen asked his parents about his illness, they told him that two of his uncles also suffer from haemophilia.
a Haemophilia is caused by a sex-linked recessive gene. Use this information to explain why only the male relatives are affected by the disease.
b Stephen was told that his mother is a 'carrier' of the disease. What does this mean?
c What are the genotypes of Stephen's brothers?

Bacterial factories

Lacking proteins

Many inherited diseases are caused by the body being unable to make an important substance – usually a **protein**. People with haemophilia lack the protein factor 8 which is needed to make the blood clot. **Pituitary dwarfism**, a disorder which results in severe underdevelopment, is caused by a lack of **growth hormone**. **Diabetes** is due to a lack of **insulin** which is needed to control the amount of glucose (sugar) in the blood.

Making proteins

People who suffer from these disorders need regular treatment with the protein that their body cannot make. Many people are diabetic so *large* amounts of the protein insulin are needed to treat them. In the past, the insulin had to be extracted from animals such as pigs and sheep. Some diabetics reacted badly to the animal insulin because animal proteins are *not identical* to human proteins. A technique developed over recent years has solved this problem by allowing *human* insulin to be made on a large scale.

The human cells that produce insulin cannot be grown easily outside the body. The cells of bacteria and other microbes can be grown on a large scale quickly and cheaply – but bacteria do not normally make insulin. By transferring human genes for making insulin into bacteria, scientists have created bacteria which do manufacture insulin – *human* insulin. This example of **genetic engineering** is shown below. Human insulin produced by bacteria is now widely available and is marketed under the name **Humulin**.

The insulin which many diabetics need to inject daily is now produced by bacteria. ▼

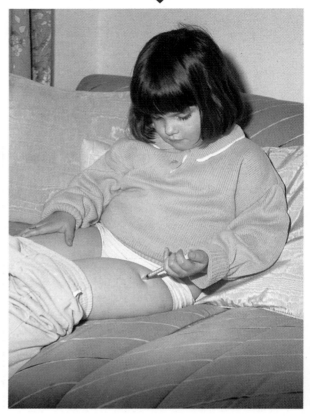

Making bacteria manufacture human insulin. ▼

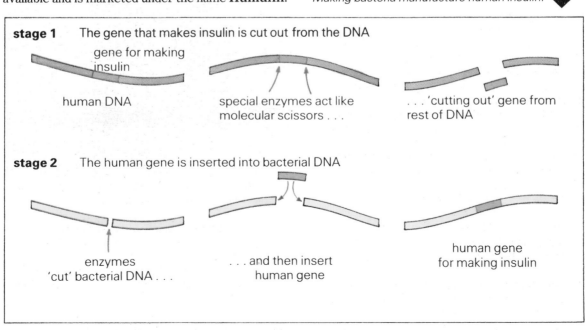

stage 1   The gene that makes insulin is cut out from the DNA

gene for making insulin

human DNA

special enzymes act like molecular scissors . . .

. . . 'cutting out' gene from rest of DNA

stage 2   The human gene is inserted into bacterial DNA

enzymes 'cut' bacterial DNA . . .

. . . and then insert human gene

human gene for making insulin

Large-scale production

Bacteria containing the human gene are grown inside huge industrial fermenters called **bioreactors**. These provide ideal conditions for the bacteria so that they grow and reproduce rapidly, forming millions of bacterial cells containing the human gene. Producing many copies of identical cells, each containing the same genes, is called **gene cloning**. Then the bacterial clones are collected, and the insulin they have made is extracted and purified.

Manufacturing human insulin (Humulin) on a large scale. ▼

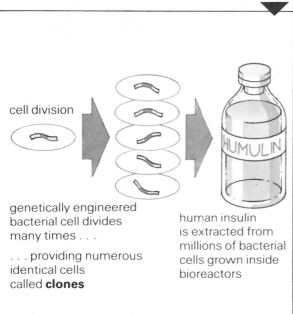

cell division

genetically engineered
bacterial cell divides
many times . . .

. . . providing numerous
identical cells
called **clones**

human insulin
is extracted from
millions of bacterial
cells grown inside
bioreactors

Cheaper and safer drugs

Through genetic engineering, bacteria can be made to produce many proteins vital to us. Human growth hormone used to be extracted from human tissue, which meant that it was extremely scarce and expensive. Nowadays human growth hormone produced by bacteria is widely available for the treatment of abnormally small children. Genetically engineered bacteria not only make drugs available in greater quantity – the drugs they produce are also *safer*. In 1985, three patients died from a virus that was present in the human tissue containing growth hormone they received. Genetic engineering has meant that more children can be given life-saving drugs which are uncontaminated with any virus.

A bioreactor must maintain the perfect environment for bacteria to thrive and reproduce. What do you think bacteria need in order to thrive? ▼

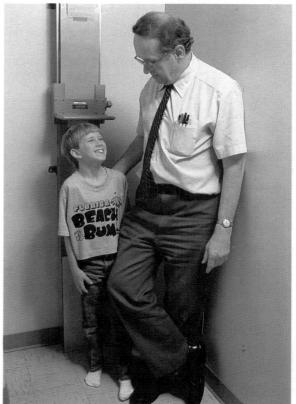

The growth hormone which this boy lacks can now be manufactured in 'bacterial factories'.

---

1 List *three* conditions that need to be controlled in bioreactors to produce the best growth of bacteria.

2 Why is factor 8 (the clotting factor lacking in haemophiliacs) made by bacteria safer to use than factor 8 extracted from human tissue?

3 Scientists can manipulate and change the genetic instructions in cells using genetic engineering.
   a What are the advantages of this process?
   b What possible disadvantages can you think of?

YOU CAN READ MORE ABOUT BLOOD GLUCOSE ON SPREAD 3.18.

4.13 *Genetic fingerprinting*

Unmistakable identity

Just as your fingerprints are unique to you, so is the pattern of genes in your DNA. Unless you are an identical twin, no one else will have a 'genetic fingerprint' exactly like yours. In 1984, scientists found a way of *identifying* sections of DNA – a technique called **genetic fingerprinting**. The technique produces a pattern that looks rather like the bar codes you see on groceries in the supermarket. Everyone has a different bar code – it is nature's own identity system.

Inheriting DNA patterns

The patterns of DNA in a father's sperm and a mother's egg mix when the sperm and egg fuse at fertilisation. So each child's genetic 'bar code' contains half the father's and half the mother's patterns.

> This diagram shows the genetic fingerprints of the members of two families. Can you see sections of DNA the children have inherited from each parent? Have *all* the children inherited sections of DNA from *both* parents? ▼

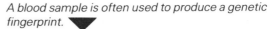

A blood sample is often used to produce a genetic fingerprint. ▼

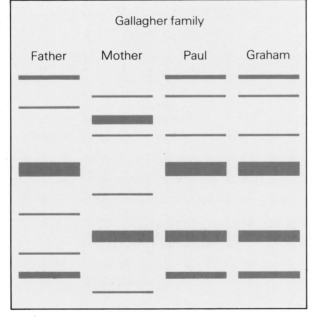

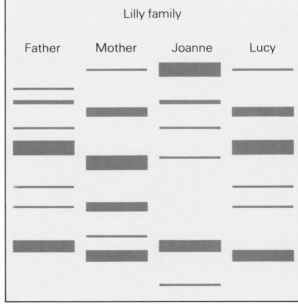

Identifying family ties

One of the first uses of genetic fingerprinting involved a boy who was born in Britain and emigrated to Ghana to live with his father. When he tried to return to this country to rejoin his mother, the immigration authorities refused to let him enter Britain. They claimed that he was not the mother's real son. The boy's genetic fingerprints showed that he shared half of the mother's DNA pattern. This evidence proved that he was her son and the authorities agreed to allow him to join his mother.

The fingerprinting process

Genetic fingerprinting was first developed by Professor Alec Jeffreys at Leicester University. The diagram shows the main stages in producing a DNA fingerprint.

The process of genetic fingerprinting.

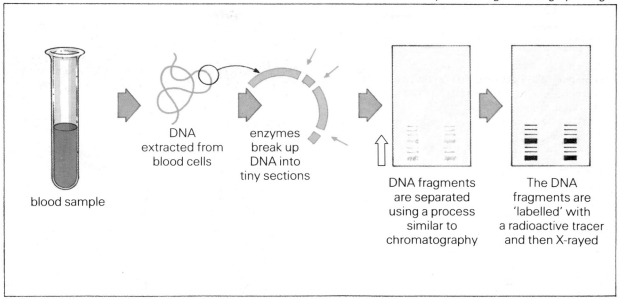

blood sample

DNA extracted from blood cells

enzymes break up DNA into tiny sections

DNA fragments are separated using a process similar to chromatography

The DNA fragments are 'labelled' with a radioactive tracer and then X-rayed

Criminal evidence

Forensic scientists examine any blood, hair, semen or other tissue found at the scene of a crime. In the past, the tissue could only give some clues about the criminal, such as his or her blood group.

Suspect 1
Suspect 2
Suspect 3
Sample from window

Now a genetic fingerprint taken from the tissue can pinpoint the offender. The 'bar code' produced from the tissue is compared with the genetic fingerprints of suspects – a match identifies the criminal, while a mismatch clears the innocent.

Three of these genetic fingerprints are from men suspected of burglary, while the other is from blood found next to a broken window used to gain entry.

Using genetic fingerprinting

The technique is now widely used in forensic science and in proving family relationships – including confirming the pedigrees of dogs and horses! Genetic fingerprinting is also a valuable tool in medicine. The success of transplant surgery depends partly on how well the organ being transplanted matches the recipient – and genetic fingerprinting can ensure the best match. The technique also helps to identify certain inherited diseases.

1. Use the genetic fingerprints of the two families shown on the opposite page to answer these questions:
   a. What can you deduce about the relationship between Paul and Graham?
   b. Joanne's mother died when she was very young. Since then her father has remarried. Explain the DNA patterns shown by Joanne and her younger sister.

2. What can you deduce about each of the burglary suspects from the evidence shown above?

3. In a recent murder hunt, the police obtained blood samples from more than 5 000 people for genetic fingerprinting. The Home Office is considering creating a data base which will contain everyone's genetic prints. Do you think that this would be a good idea? Give reasons for your answer.

4.14 Building proteins

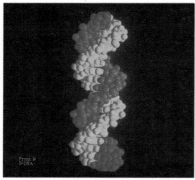

A model of a DNA molecule ▲ showing the two strands twisted round each other in a spiral or helix.

Revealing the structure of DNA

Genetic engineering, genetic fingerprinting and other recent developments in genetics were made possible by the discovery of the **structure of DNA**. In the early 1950s scientists knew that DNA carries coded instructions for making proteins, but no-one knew *how* the code worked. The discovery of DNA's structure by James Watson and Francis Crick in 1953 was one of the major advances in science. Watson and Crick pieced together the findings of other scientists researching DNA and arrived at the now-famous **double helix structure**. They suggested that each molecule of DNA has two long strands twisted around each other like a spiral staircase.

*Four kinds of bases link the backbones – A (which stands for adenine), T (thymine), C (cytosine) and G (guanine). A always pairs with T, while C always pairs with G. This is called **specific base pairing**. ▼*

The backbone of each strand is joined to the other strand by bases. ▼

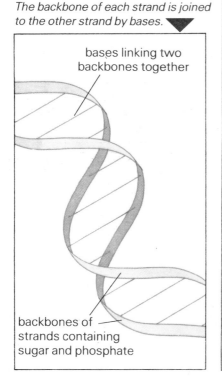

bases linking two backbones together

backbones of strands containing sugar and phosphate

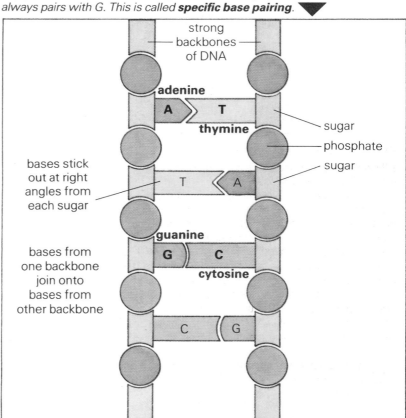

strong backbones of DNA

adenine
A — T
thymine

sugar
phosphate
sugar

bases stick out at right angles from each sugar

T — A

bases from one backbone join onto bases from other backbone

guanine
G — C
cytosine

C — G

A scientist called Chargaff was working on the structure of DNA at the same time as Watson and Crick. He found out the amount of each of the four DNA bases that is present in different organisms. Some of his findings are shown in this table.

Watson and Crick used Chargaff's data when putting forward their model of DNA. How do Chargaff's findings support their model of DNA?

	Relative amount of each base			
	adenine	thymine	cytosine	guamine
Salmon DNA	30	30	20	20
Mouse DNA	29	27	22	21
Human DNA	30	29	19	19

Breaking the code

After Watson and Crick had worked out the structure of DNA, they went on to find out how the coded information in DNA is used by living organisms to make proteins. They discovered that the *order of the bases* in each strand of DNA forms the code. Proteins are made up of chemicals called **amino acids**. The order of the bases in DNA controls the order in which amino acids are joined together during the making of proteins. By controlling the synthesis of proteins, DNA determines the inherited characteristics of each individual.

The type and order of amino acids in a protein are determined by the DNA code. ▼

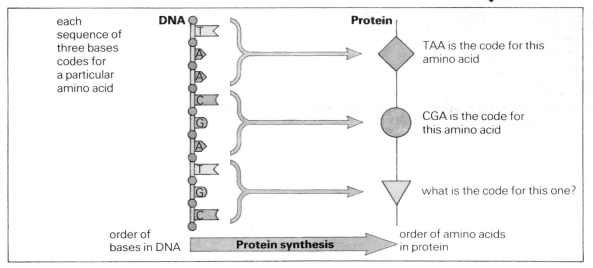

each sequence of three bases codes for a particular amino acid

DNA

Protein

TAA is the code for this amino acid

CGA is the code for this amino acid

what is the code for this one?

order of bases in DNA → **Protein synthesis** → order of amino acids in protein

Amino acids – the buildings blocks

All proteins are polymers (long, chain molecules) made of chains of amino acids. There are just 20 amino acids found in proteins, but they can be arranged in billions of different ways. Every living organism contains a large number of proteins. You contain about 100 000 different proteins, each carrying out an essential job in keeping you alive and well. The properties of each protein depend on the order and types of amino acids that make up its structure. A protein may not do the same job if only *one* amino acid in its structure is changed. DNA controls *which* amino acids will be in the protein and the *order* in which they will be joined.

Amino acids are like an alphabet for making proteins. If the amino acids are put together in a different order, a different protein is 'spelt out'. ▼

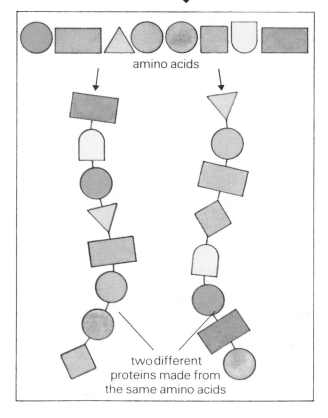

amino acids

two different proteins made from the same amino acids

1
  a Explain what 'specific base pairing' means.
  b The bases in a strand of DNA are in the order:

        A C T T G C C T A A

    What will the order of bases be on the other strand of DNA?

2 A gene can be described as the sequence of bases in DNA that controls the synthesis of a protein.
  a A protein was found to consist of 100 amino acids. How many bases would there be in the gene that makes this protein?
  b Predict how the structure of the protein might change if just one of the bases in the gene was changed for another one.

4.15 Replicating genes

Copying the code

All the characteristics that you inherited from your parents are controlled by the sequence of bases in the DNA in your cells. DNA can form exact copies of itself so that the coded instructions for making proteins can be passed on to new cells and new individuals. The coded instructions that make up each gene are copied each time a cell divides. Every cell in your body contains an exact copy of the genes that you inherited from your parents. This diagram shows how a DNA molecule copies itself during **replication**. ▶

The order of bases in each original strand controls the order of bases in the new molecule. So the two new molecules of DNA formed are identical to the original molecule. ▶

Making new cells

DNA is contained in chromosomes surrounded by a protein coat for protection. New DNA and new chromosomes are made during cell division. So the *amount* of DNA in cells *changes* during cell division.

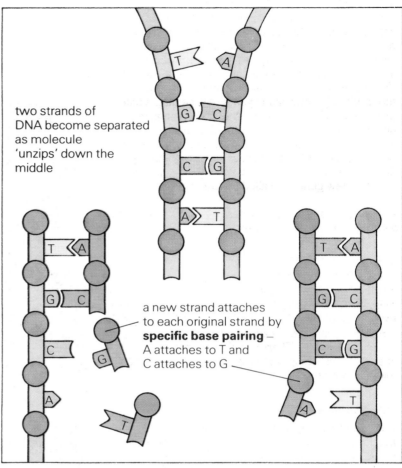

two strands of DNA become separated as molecule 'unzips' down the middle

a new strand attaches to each original strand by **specific base pairing** – A attaches to T and C attaches to G

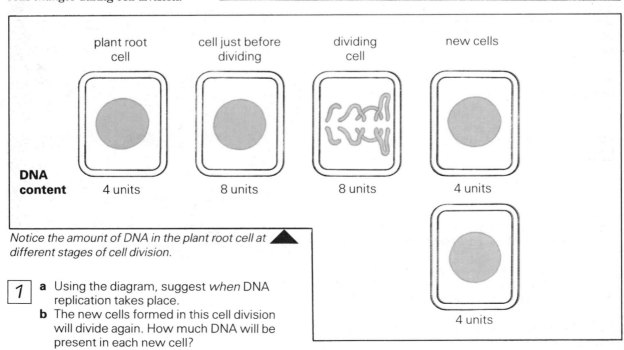

plant root cell	cell just before dividing	dividing cell	new cells
DNA content 4 units	8 units	8 units	4 units

4 units

Notice the amount of DNA in the plant root cell at ▲ *different stages of cell division.*

1 **a** Using the diagram, suggest *when* DNA replication takes place.
   b The new cells formed in this cell division will divide again. How much DNA will be present in each new cell?

Making incorrect copies

When animals and plants reproduce, genes are passed to the next generation through gametes (*see 4.3*). This means that it is *usually* possible to predict patterns of inheritance. But sometimes completely **new varieties** of offspring are produced. For example, budgies, which have been kept as pet birds for many years, always used to have green feathers. When they bred, their offspring had green feathers too. Suddenly, after many years of breeding, a blue-feathered variety appeared. A sudden change in phenotype such as this is the result of **gene mutation**. It occurs when the base sequence in DNA that makes a gene is not replicated *exactly* during cell division, creating a *new* form of the gene. Individuals with the new gene are called **mutants**.

The first blue budgies were a result of a mutation in the gene coding for feather colour.

Causing mutation

Certain factors known as **mutagenic factors** increase the chance of mutation. Exposure to ionising radiation or to ultraviolet rays in sunlight can increase the chance of mutation occurring. Some forms of **skin cancer** are mutations caused by prolonged exposure to strong sunlight. There are also mutagenic chemicals, including certain dyes, food additives and food preservatives.

Forming new varieties

A new variety may appear if the mutant gene is *inherited*. This can only happen when the mutation occurs in *gamete-producing* cells. The majority of new genes created by mutation are recessive. So a new phenotype will not appear unless *two* mutant genes occur together – that is, unless the mutant gene is inherited from *both* parents.

Which tomato would you choose? Apart from the normal red, there are many colour varieties produced by mutation.

2. If the DNA content of a human body cell is 20 units, what amount of DNA will be found in
   a a human sperm cell?
   b a zygote?

3. Suggest explanations for the following.
   a The incidence of skin cancer in people living in the UK has increased over recent years.
   b In South Africa, skin cancer is very rare among black African inhabitants and more common in people of European descent.

4. Why do most mutations only appear many generations after gene mutation?

YOU CAN READ MORE ABOUT THE EFFECTS OF IONISING RADIATION ON THE BODY IN CHEMISTRY BOOK, SPREAD 3.11

Index

Heinemann Educational,
a division of Heinemann Educational Books Ltd,
Halley Court, Jordan Hill, Oxford, OX2 8EJ

OXFORD LONDON EDINBURGH
MADRID ATHENS BOLOGNA PARIS
MELBOURNE SYDNEY AUCKLAND
SINGAPORE TOKYO
IBADAN NAIROBI HARARE GABORONE
PORTSMOUTH NH (USA)

Includes material from *The Sciences for GCSE* first
published 1989–91

This edition first published 1992

ISBN 0 435 57542 2

Designed, illustrated and phototypeset by Gecko
Ltd, Bicester, Oxon

Printed in Spain by Mateu Cromo

The authors and publishers would like to thank the
following for permission to use photographs.

Cover photo: Oxford Scientific Films/James
Robinson

Other photos: page 2, top and contents page,
Petit Format/Nestle/SPL; middle, J Allan Cash;
bottom, Avril Ramage/Oxford Scientific Films;
page 3, top, Kathie Atkinson/Oxford Scientific
Films; middle, Ronald Toms/Oxford Scientific
Films; bottom and contents page, J Allan Cash;
page 5, GeoScience Features; page 8, Holt
Studios; Page 12, Holt Studios; page 14, top,
Greenpeace/Dorreboon; bottom, ZEFA/Janoud;
page 15 and contents page, NHPA/Laurie
Campbell; page 17, top, The Hulton Library;
bottom, SPL; page 19, RT Smith/RSPB; page 20,
Frank Lane Agency/BB Cassals; page 21, Frank
Lane Agency/Roger Wilmhurst; page 23, Frank
Lane Agency/J C Allen; page 26, GeoScience
Features; page 33, left, Hutchinson Library/Chris
Pemberton; right; Barnaby's Picture Library; page
35, GeoScience Features; page 36, Holt Studios;
page 38, Holt Studios; page 40, left, GeoScience
Features; middle, NHPA/J Shaw; right, SPL/Dr J
Burgess; bottom, NHPA/S Dalton; page 41,
bottom, SPL/Petit Format; page 44, Vision
International/Anthea Sieveling; page 46(×2),
Barnaby's Picture Library; page 52, top, Barnaby's
Picture Library; bottom, J Allan Cash; page 53,
Sporting Pictures Ltd; page 54(×2), Trevor Hill,
page 56, SPL; page 58, Sally & Richard Greenhill;
page 59, top, J Allan Cash; bottom, Sporting
Pictures Ltd; page 60, Sally & Richard Greenhill;
page 62, Barnaby's Picture Library; page 67, SPL/
H Morgan; page 70, Environmental Picture
Library/J Holmes; page 71, Environmental Picture
Library/Chris Rose; page 74, Sefton Picture
Library; page 76, top, NHPL/S Dalton; bottom,
GeoScience Features; page 79, SPL/CNRI; page
80, NHPA/E James; page 81, NHPA/S Dalton;
page 83, SPL/Petit Format; page 84, top, SPL/J
Stevenson; bottom, SPL/J Widel; page 86, top,
SPL/Petit Format; left, SPL/J Howard; right, SPL/J
Stevenson; page 87, SPL/A Bartel; page 88,
ZEFA; page 89, top, SPL/Andrew McClenaghan;
bottom and contents page, Topham Picture
Source/UPPA; page 90, GeoScience Features;
page 91, left, NHPA/J Shaw; right, GeoScience
Features; page 92, SPL/J Hesteltine; page 93,
SPL/A Hart Davis; page 94, top, Sally & Richard
Greenhill; bottom, AllSport Photographic Ltd/Tony
Duffy; page 95, SPL; page 96, Sally & Richard
Greenhill; page 97, SPL; page 98, top, Sally &
Richard Greenhill; bottom, SPL; page 100 and
101, SPL; page 105, SPL; page 107, NHPA/Roger
Peny; page 110(×3), Frank Lane Picture Agency;
page 111, Holt Studios Ltd; pages 112, 114,
116–8, 120, SPL; page 123, top, Frank Lane
Picture Library; bottom, NHPA/M Savonius;